ONCE UPON
A RHYME

IMAGINATION FOR
A NEW GENERATION

West Midlands Vol II
Edited by Steve Twelvetree

 Young**Writers**

First published in Great Britain in 2004 by:
Young Writers
Remus House
Coltsfoot Drive
Peterborough
PE2 9JX
Telephone: 01733 890066
Website: www.youngwriters.co.uk

SB ISBN 1 84460 502 7

Foreword

Young Writers was established in 1991 and has been passionately devoted to the promotion of reading and writing in children and young adults ever since. The quest continues today. Young Writers remains as committed to engendering the fostering of burgeoning poetic and literary talent as ever.

This year's Young Writers competition has proven as vibrant and dynamic as ever and we are delighted to present a showcase of the best poetry from across the UK. Each poem has been carefully selected from a wealth of *Once Upon A Rhyme* entries before ultimately being published in this, our twelfth primary school poetry series.

Once again, we have been supremely impressed by the overall high quality of the entries we have received. The imagination, energy and creativity which has gone into each young writer's entry made choosing the best poems a challenging and often difficult but ultimately hugely rewarding task - the general high standard of the work submitted amply vindicating this opportunity to bring their poetry to a larger appreciative audience.

We sincerely hope you are pleased with our final selection and that you will enjoy *Once Upon A Rhyme West Midlands Vol II* for many years to come.

Contents

Holly Georgina Cant (10)   1

Bentley Drive School
Rebecca Coley (10)   2
Charlotte Gould (8)   2
Sophie Connell (11)   3
Louis Spalding (10)   3
Karenjeet Chahal (10)   4
Shaquille Ologitere (10)   4
Laura Mills (11)   5
Jennifer Chapman (10)   6
Tehmina Ahmed (10)   7

Christ Church CE Primary School
Adam Clements (10)   7
Tara Pitt (10)   8
Jasdeep Kaur (9)   8
Chloe Derry (10)   9
Chanel McKenzie (7)   9
Amy Bannister (9)   10
Jordan Archer (10)   10
Jason Cook (8)   10
Rachael Allman (8)   11
Charlotte Jansen (8)   11
Deborah Jones (8)   11
Alice Whittaker (8)   12
Craig Boughey (8)   12
Ryan Birkett (9)   13
Jake Stanton (11)   13
Laura Arnold (10)   14
Jordan Longdon (8)   14
Charlotte Wiggin (10)   14
Jemma Ball (8)   15
Demi Jeffrey (9)   15
Callum Cheatle (8)   15
Alice Jansen (9)   16
Thomas Vigrass (7)   16
Danielle Murphy (7)   17
Samantha Holmes (10)   17

Jade Porter (8)   18
Sophie Gunter (7)   18
Luke Antill (7)   18
Joshua Gilbody (9)   19
John Harris (10)   19
Jack Marlow (8)   19
Peter Allsop (10)   20
Reece Caunt (7)   20

Cooper & Jordan Primary School
Michael Lawrence (8)   20
Madeline Thorn (8)   21
Danielle Talbot (9)   21
Matthew Bryant (8)   21
Max Standerwick (8)   22
David Rea-Gardner (9)   22
Holly Sheldon (9)   22
Andrew Munns (9)   23
George Morgan (8)   23
Olivia Moseley (8)   23
Sam Jones (8)   24
Bradley Matthews (8)   24
Matthew Kirby (9)   24
Bethany Jones (8)   25
Joshua Wilson (8)   25
Eliott Cook (8)   25
Amy Hawes (8)   26
Rebecca Garbett (9)   26
Thomas Fielder (9)   26
Jessica Green (9)   27
Samuel Cole (8)   27
Megan Hughes (8)   27
Reece Lewis (8)   28
Jamie Evans (9)   28
Lauren Hanslow (8)   29
Jacob Marklew (8)   29

Curdworth Primary School
Hannah Whittle (10)   29
Joe McKenna (10)   30
Freisha Patel (10)   31

Tom Powell (10) — 32
Sam Rhodes (10) — 33
Lucy Fisher (10) — 34
Rhys Yates (11) — 34
Stephanie Downes (11) — 35
Nitesh Chamdal (10) — 35
Jake Gallagher (11) — 36
Rebecca Woodward (10) — 36
Lucy Foster (11) — 37
Charlotte Lacey (10) — 38

Fairhaven Primary School
Emily Cope (10) — 38
Jessica Knott-Packwood (10) — 39
Joshua Pagett (10) — 39
Emily Hill (10) — 40
Alice Mason (10) — 40
Lucy Rogers (10) — 41
Georgia Kirkham (10) — 41
Charlotte McEvoy (10) — 42

Four Oaks Junior School
Justine Belcher (9) — 42
Samuel Commander (9) — 43
Gemma Smith (8) — 43
Georgina Woodward (8) — 44
Elizabeth McNab (9) — 44
Simone Gerald (8) — 45
Hannah Skelding (9) — 45
Greg Mansell (8) — 46
Emma Biles (8) — 46
Emily Heatherley (8) — 47
Matthew Watts (9) — 47
Matthew Goodall (9) — 48
Oliver Smith (9) — 49
Rosie Wilkes (8) — 50
Nicole Alexandra Parsons (8) — 50
Harry Emberson — 51
Cameron Edkins (9) — 51
William Richards (8) — 52
Harry James John Eady (9) — 52

Danny Nicoll (8)	53
Chloe Josephine Swadkin (9)	53
Elliot George Cotterill (11)	54
Luke Woodward (9)	54
Jack Cartwright (8)	55
Antonia Mander (8)	55
Alex Duffy (10)	56
Natalie Parkman (8)	56
Katie Hearnden (10)	57
Connor McElroy (8)	57
Eden Hyland (9)	58
Aaron Dhadli (8)	58
Rachel Parkman (11)	59
Liam Haigh (9)	59
Robert Slann (10)	60
Isabella Barber (10)	61
Erica Powell (10)	62
Charlie Hughes (10)	63
George Howells (9)	64
Ben Tipson (9)	65
Michael Hogg (11)	66
Satnam Minhas & Michael Heslington (10)	66
Steven Micklewright (11)	67
Danny Knowles (10)	67
Jack Etherton & Dexter Ealing (10)	68
Josh Wearing & Tom Silverton (11)	68
Mischa Howell (11)	69
Hoi Yan Wong (10)	69
Jack Moore (10)	70
Hannah Ward (10)	70
Nadine Haskey (11)	71
Oliver Swadkin (10)	71
Chelsea Binyon (10)	72
Stephanie Shoesmith (10)	72
Kanar Talabani (11)	73
Stephen Davey (10)	73
Christina Loizou-Socratous (10)	74
Ruth Awunor (11)	74
Megan Brett (10)	75
Sarah Kitteridge (8)	75
Alice Brooks (10)	76
Lucy Palmer (9)	76

Alex Maxwell-Keys (9)	77
Laura Davies-Hale (10)	77
Harriette Watkins (10)	78
Grace McDowall (10)	78
Laura Cleveley (9)	79
Ellie Goodman (9)	79
Sam Neal (10)	80
Melissa Chiam (9)	81
Amie Haigh (11)	82
Haleigh Mathews (10)	82
Joe Wright (10)	83
Jacob Beechey (10)	83
Luke Winkless (10)	84
Robyn Coles (10)	84
Richard Shotton (10)	85
James Quance (9)	85
Jordan Arnett (9)	86
Jack Whiting (9)	86
Matthew Litwinowicz (9)	87
Katie Etherton (8)	87

Great Bridge Primary School

Charlotte Montgomery (10)	88
Tyler Durnall (11)	88
Jade Wyatt (10)	89
Samantha Bates (10)	89
Charlotte Wyatt (9)	90
Zoë Allen (9)	91
Charlotte Cox (9)	92
Daniel Leatherland (10)	92
Katie Williams (10)	93
Megan Wildman (9)	93
Kevin Clayton (10)	94
Sundeep Kaur (10)	94
Daniel Bell (11)	95
Laura Summers (10)	95
Daniel Weaver (10)	95
Paige Byrne (9)	96
Hollie Willett (9)	96
Devinder Sangoo (11)	97
Ritesh Patel (10)	97

Kyle Guest (10)	98
Christopher James (11)	98
Liam Rickards (9)	98
Georgina Richards (11)	99
Kirsty Hipkins (11)	99
Paige Moore (10)	99
Sharondeep Shergill (10)	100
Lucie Bonehill (11)	100
Jasmeena Samrai (10)	101
Stacey Guest (11)	101
Halima Atika Hussain (11)	102
Jordanne Doody (11)	102
Sylvia Dias (11)	103
Daniel Norton (10)	103
Amie-Lea Sambrook (10)	104
Arfana Hussain (11)	104
Ajay Singh (10)	105
Rachel Bennett (10)	105

Hatherton Lane Primary School

Dale Peach (9)	106
Sean Pinnington (9)	106
Demi-Lee Ranford (9)	107
Stefen Dukes (9)	107
Keelli Davis (10)	108
Chloe O'Brien (9)	108
Jonathon Duckett (10)	109
Daniel Fellows (9)	109
Leanne Wootton (10)	110
Ashley Harvey (10)	110
Thomas Corrigan (10)	111
Amber-Jade Bennett (10)	111
Mathew Rollinson (8)	112
Thomas Wain (10)	112
Joanna Waddison (9)	113
Matthew Jones (9)	113
Laura Fisher (9)	114
Laura Missen (10)	114
Luke Talbot (10)	115
Amy Henworth (9)	115
Lucy Hunt (9)	116

Melissa Parsons (9)	117
Haley Bagnall (9)	118
Nicholas Edwards (10)	118
Rebekah Harvey (10)	119
Ashley Silvester (10)	119
Bradley Sanders (11)	120
Ryan Lycett (10)	120
Lauren Stanton (8)	121
Damon Harvey (8)	121
Danielle Ball (11)	122
Louise Richards (9)	122
Emma Pringle (9)	123
Ryan Bolstridge (8)	123
Jack Healy (10)	124
Charlotte Rutter (8)	124
Jade Mansell (11)	125
Shannon Owen (10)	125
Stacey Sedgwick (10)	126
Kimberly James (9)	126
Jade Higgins (11)	127
Scott Lawton (11)	127
Luke Bickley (11)	128
Shannon O'Brien (8)	128
Joshua Smith (10)	129
Lewis Guttridge (9)	129
Thomas Williams (11)	130
Courtney Green (9)	130
Amy Jones (11)	131
Ryan Stanley (8)	131
Jodie Butler (10)	132
Charlotte Joseph (9)	132
Laura Cox (9)	133
Jordan Broomhall (8)	133
Gemma Hales (10)	134
Matthew Instone (9)	134
Chelsea Whitticase (8)	135
Jodie Banks (9)	135
Luke Wilding (8)	135
Joshua Hartshorne (8)	136
Tom Harding (8)	136
Timmy Richards (9)	136
Jordan Higgins (9)	137

Kayne Humphries (9)	137
Jamie Garratley (9)	137

Lakeside Primary School

Abraham Gordon (8)	138
Rosie Dudley (7)	138
Daniel Eagleton (7)	139
Daniel Bradley (8)	139
Bethany Stokes (7)	140
Verity North (8)	140
Sam MacDonald (8)	141
Ellis Lucas (9)	141
Ciara Evans (10)	142
Cassie-Ann Smith (9)	142
Joseph Stevens (8)	143
Matthew Dunn (11)	143
Ashley Williams (10)	144
Nathan Garner (9)	144
Amy Page (11)	144
Tristan Hughes (8)	145
Andrew Bowering (9)	145
Natalie Lloyd (10)	145
Alexandra Jackson (10)	146
Jordan Evans (8)	146
Lauren Gibbons (8)	146
Sophie Wilson (9)	147
Kirsty Clarke (10)	147

Little Bloxwich CE Primary School

Eleanor Whitehouse (7)	147
Damon Cotton (8)	148
Liam Christian (8)	148
Jessica Jillian Price (7)	149
Ryan Parker (8)	149
Charlotte Jackson (8)	150
Gemma Greenwood (7)	150
Megan Chapman (7)	151
Jack Hill (7)	151
Rebecca Stringer (8)	152
Aidan Mansell (7)	152
Lauren Hunt (8)	153

Liam Froggatt (7)   153
Daniel Beale (7)   154
Chloe Harper (7)   154
Navneet Budesha (10)   155
Luke Clark (9)   155
Tom Burden (10)   155
Reanne Simone Langston (10)   156
Thomas Pritchard (9)   156
Katie Richards (10)   156
Alysha Harris (10)   157
Stephen Witton (10)   157
Guy Buchanan (10)   157
Oliver Chapman (9)   158
Thomas Spencer (10)   158
Rebecca Dennis (10)   158
Samuel Hubble (9)   159
Emily Pearce (9)   159
Elizabeth Dennis (10)   159
Joshua Reynolds (9)   160
Luke Povey (10)   160
Sophie James (9)   160
Natalie Danielle Neale (10)   161
Jessica Hancox (8)   161

Lodge CP School

Zobia Kausar (10)   161
Amina Khanom (10)   162
Sarah Ali (9)   162
Samantha Gill (9)   162
Briony Scarlett (11)   163
Amardeep Kaur (11)   163
Abdullah Choudhury (10)   164
Sonia Suman (11)   164
Fauzia Jabeen (10)   165
Nurjahan Aktar (8)   165
Shelina Hussain (7)   166
Shaheen Malik (11)   166
Jaya Chohan (8)   166
Humayra Kamal (9)   167
Kiran Balaggan (10)   167
Gagandeep Dhillon (10)   168

Priya Balagan (7)   168
Asimah Kauser (10)   169
Anisa Akhtar (10)   169
Habiba Begum (10)   170
Yahya Saeed (10)   170
Ravinder Deol (10)   170

Mayfield Preparatory School

Benjamin Wheeler (11)   171
Sukhpreet Dosanjh (10)   171
Olivia Ireson (11)   171
Charles Isherwood (11)   172
Navreen Mangat (10)   173
Madhav Bakshi (10)   174
Manveer Mahal (10)   174
Elisha Edgeworth (10)   175
Colin Hock (10)   175
Alice Holtom (10)   176
Mahima Kharabanda (10)   176
Philippa Mills (10)   177
Ben Watson (10)   177
Anjali Parekh (11)   178
Shamail Khan (11)   178
Natasha Patel (11)   178
Raman Sidhu (9)   179
Thomas Greatrex (9)   179
Nika Norman (9)   179
Jasdeep Bath (10)   180
Laura Marshall (11)   180
Emily Ratcliffe (9)   181
Amrita Dhallu (10)   181
Abigail Higginbottom (9)   182
Jasmehar Mavi (9)   182
Rishika Patel (9)   182
Matthew Fielden (9)   183
Bethany Marshall (9)   183
Charlotte Underhill (9)   183
Japjeet Kulair (9)   184
Melissa Kirkland-Swann (10)   184
Chandon Chahal (10)   185
Jonathan Mahon (10)   185

Sara Farooqui (10)	186
Arjan Drayton-Chana (9)	186
Ashveen Kohli (9)	186
Adam Patel (8)	187
Philippa Southern (9)	187
Emma Barker (8)	187
Gavan Nijjar (8)	188
Shannon Chatha (8)	188
Richard Ng (8)	188
Jagveer Mahal (9)	189
Miles Carlisle (8)	189
Jonathan Duckett (9)	189
Robert Angell (9)	190
Jordon Sproule (8)	190
Virron Chahal (8)	190
Philippa Watson (8)	191

Rough Hay Primary School

Abigail Page (10)	191
Sandeep Sandhu (11)	191
Tanjina Ali (11)	192
Martin Rollason (11)	192
Mark Kendall (11)	192
Carol Brooks (11)	193
Ryce Duffus (10)	193
Gemma Hayward (11)	193
Deanna Banks (10)	194
Charlotte Lawley (11)	194
Jack Watts (11)	194
Jade Perry (10)	195

Woodlands Primary School

Alannah Cossey (8)	195
Bobby Carver (10)	195
Courtney Guy (9)	196
Joseph Davies (10)	196
James Moore (9)	196
Natalie Carless (9)	197
Lee Tranter (9)	197
Kimberley Smith (8)	197
Ryan O'Brien (11)	198

Jodie Aris (11)   198
Kayleigh Hill (8)   199

The Poems

Love

Love is as red as a sweet, fragrant rose
As green as the grass that tickles your nose.
Love's as precious as a great tale of old
A magical story I've just been told.
Love is as strong as the wind in a gale
As beautiful as lovebirds so graceful and pale.
Love is as wide as the sea is so blue
Black as a panther, this really is true.
Love is as bright as the sky through the day
Soft as the clouds that drift far away.

Love is as gold and as twinkly as stars
And as distant as Earth is to Mars.
Love is as cute as a lamb born in spring
Mighty and powerful as our Lord is king.
Love is as special as hearts made of gold
As fragile as orchids that I have been sold.
Love is as silver as trails from a snail
Long and furry as a soft kitten's tail.
Love is calming as a thrush's sweet song
Sung through each day of the summertime long.

Love's so peaceful as a midsummer day
Bright as the sun and as fresh as new hay.
Love is as juicy as a soft blueberry
Strong and delicious like a glass of sherry.
Love can be cold as the snow falling fast,
Smooth as the snowflakes go waltzing past,
Love can be painful, it can be kind
So long as you're honest, love you will find.

Holly Georgina Cant (10)

The Hamster

People chatting away
While I sit here, alone.
You fill your faces with food -
Me, I just have lettuce and water for survival.
Asking for a bit of respect
Is that a lot?
Munching on my lettuce
Drinking the drop of water, I have left,
If you want someone to pamper -
Pamper me!
Brush my marmalade fur
Stroke me!
But no! Occasionally you pick me up
Your dagger nails digging into my fur.
You place me in my ball
Rolling me across the kitchen floor.
The sunshine from the window
Blinds me while you are watching TV.
Suddenly, vice-like hands grip me
I am back in my cage
Suffocating!

Rebecca Coley (10)
Bentley Drive School

Lunchtime With Lions

King of the land,
Creature of killing
Maker of life or death
The boss of the African plains.
Camouflaged in the yellow grass
The lion chases the unlucky visitor.
The daggers stab the prey and
As they drop dead
The lion
Bites.

Charlotte Gould (8)
Bentley Drive School

The Spider's Questions

Quickly, I scuttle across the floor
Trying not to get spotted.
My eight little legs, as black as coal
Carry me along.
To you I may look scary and you may run
But all I do is search
Not meaning to cause any harm.
Then I see them -
The monstrous birds
Fed by you
But still, they eat me and my friends.
You break my webs
Which I have spent all night making.
Why?
I don't ask for a lot -
Just care
And thought.

Sophie Connell (11)
Bentley Drive School

Survival

My long pointed beak
Used as a tool
For digging my brown wings
And gliding through the forest
Searching for a place to live.
My young are afraid
Of the gigantic machine
Which approaches our home.
I keep thinking everything will be alright
But it's not!
They're destroying my family, once again.
Lurching towards us
The gleaming metal steals our home.
All we ask for is care and thought!

Louis Spalding (10)
Bentley Drive School

My Life Is A Computer

The sun in my face, bright and shiny,
Making my face all funny.
I haven't been used in weeks
I feel so lonely with no one to talk to
All my life, wasting away.

I hear footsteps coming towards me,
Then in front of me, a teenager awaits.
I am so happy
But now my nightmare really starts to begin.

Those dirty, sticky hands, scraping my face,
My body being pushed in and out
With that constant tapping.
Now hearing shouts and screams,
Into the repair shop
Where my life begins again.

Karenjeet Chahal (10)
Bentley Drive School

A Story From The Heart

All I do is flutter my wings and peck
Do you see any harm in that?
All I want is respect.
I do my job, day after day
This is like boot camp for me!
Foxes try to eat me and my family
When I have chicks I have to hide them
From the stupid man,
He takes them and sells them.

Suddenly a huge black shadow blocks my view
It is the farmer's vicious daughter.
She doesn't need me
She's well fed - unlike me, eating petty seeds
That don't fill me.
All I need is care, thought and safety.

Shaquille Ologitere (10)
Bentley Drive School

The Spider

Silently, I scurry across the floor
My eight tiny legs carry me along.
I ask for nothing,
Not one thing, except for care
Which is very rare.
My small black body frightens so many,
Although I'm harmless and friendly.

Suddenly, a huge black shadow towers over me,
It's you again -
Holding your lethal weapon,
Yesterday's newspaper, rolled and ready for attack.
I scurry along faster
But it's no use.
Your giant footsteps are like huge claps of thunder.
My life
So young
Yet nearly over,
Because of you!

Laura Mills (11)
Bentley Drive School

Tigers

Silently I creep across the ground,
Looking for my prey,
Feeling the rough earth under my paws,
My yellow eyes, wide, focus on my future food.
I breathe quietly
Showing my razor sharp teeth
Like daggers in my mouth.

Then I hear a bang, a gunshot
All I want is peace in the territory
No guns.
All I get is my family separated -
It hurts so much,
My heart pounds with anger.
Hunters!
Out looking, ready to shoot us.
All I ask for is privacy
Leave us be.
Care and peace - that's all we need.

Jennifer Chapman (10)
Bentley Drive School

Cat

Silently I creep from corner
To corner,
Trying not to make a sound.
In search of a brown creature
With a long pink tail.
For this, people stroke me,
But that's the only time
They care.
I ask for very little -
To be stroked
And food and water to be put before me.
Suddenly, the dreaded moment comes
When a dark shadow lurks over me
Getting ready to pounce,
Saliva dripping from its mouth
Showing its razor-like teeth.
I run to my home for safety.

Tehmina Ahmed (10)
Bentley Drive School

The Bully

The bully makes everyone sad,
The bully is very bad,
He makes you hide behind a wall
Hits you with a very hard ball.
The bully steals all your things
A guy who laughs at you and sings.

A bully is a horrible germ
Who makes you quiver and burn
A bully has a nasty bite
Getting into every fight.
A bully is a trouble maker
A bully is a child hater.

Adam Clements (10)
Christ Church CE Primary School

Stop Bullying

Stop bullying!
Victims will start worrying
      It starts with a punch
      Then there's another bunch.

Tell the teacher
About this horrible creature!
      Then it's the kick
      The bullies take the mick.

Tell your friends
Or this disaster never ends.
      Because how did it start?
      It's just like a devil's dart.

Stop bullying!
Victims will start worrying,
      Let's all be mates,
      Like soda and cakes!

Tara Pitt (10)
Christ Church CE Primary School

Friendship Never Dies

Friendship that will never die
Remember to never lie
If we fall out, it won't last
Every day we have a blast.
Never say I hate you, though it
Doesn't really mater if we do.
Soon regret what we've said
Happily talking on the phone in bed.
If we shout at each other, we will cry
Please remember friendships will never die.

Jasdeep Kaur (9)
Christ Church CE Primary School

Bullying

Bullies are horrible
Bullies are bad
When you come home you
Feel sad.

Bullying is naughty
Bully is unfriendly
When you come home you
Feel mad.

Bullying hurts you
Bullying makes you cry
When you come home you
Feel glad.

Chloe Derry (10)
Christ Church CE Primary School

Summer Holiday

I love the summer, it's really hot
I like to play in the swimming pool a lot.
When it's summer, I go on holiday,
I go to the beach with my best friend Screech.
When it's summer it's always fun because I always sit
in the boiling sun.
I love the hot sand boiling on the ground,
there's not a sound.
I love to go splashing in the bright sea,
I always watch the bumblebees.
I love to make sandcastles but they
always fall down and for some reason they turn brown.
I just love it when it's summer.

Chanel McKenzie (7)
Christ Church CE Primary School

Out Of My Window

The snow is falling
The daytime's boring,
The summer's gone
The time is moving on.

The snow is slow,
The ground is white.
The plants are dying,
It's cold at night.

Amy Bannister (9)
Christ Church CE Primary School

Friends

F riends never break promises
R eally helpful
I have had good times
E veryone has friends
N o one is ever lonely
D elighted, as your friend saves you
S aying you are their best friend.

Jordan Archer (10)
Christ Church CE Primary School

Spring, Spring, Spring

S pring, spring, spring
P etals grow back on flowers
R hyming a lot about spring
I like planting flowers a lot
N ight-time I get my water ready
G oing out to water my plants
    Spring, spring, spring.

Jason Cook (8)
Christ Church CE Primary School

Spring

Sweet birds sing along
To the sweetest song
Snow falls
Making snowmen tall.
Having friends round to tea,
Eating and drinking, good to see.
Swimming in your swimming pool,
Having ice cubes, very cool.

Rachael Allman (8)
Christ Church CE Primary School

The Dreadful Rain

The weather is cruel outside,
And the rain is coming down.
I look out of my bedroom
I want to get outside.
I wait and wait but then I sleep
I'm locked within my dream
The rain pours down the wall.
I wish that the raindrops could hear
My call.

Charlotte Jansen (8)
Christ Church CE Primary School

Days Of The Week

On Monday I can see snow,
On Tuesday I can see snow again.
On Wednesday I can see rain
On Thursday I can see hail and
On Friday, I can see the sun.

Deborah Jones (8)
Christ Church CE Primary School

Days Of The Week

On Monday it's a snow day
On Monday it's a fun day.
On Monday it's a good day
While the snow starts to go away.

On Tuesday it's a blue day,
On Tuesday, it's a work day,
On Tuesday it's a good day
While people come out to play.

On Wednesday it's Ben's day
On Wednesday it's a friend's day,
On Wednesday it's a good day
While your friends go out to play.

On Thursday it's a sun day
On Thursday it's going away
On Thursday it's a good day.

On Friday it's a go-away day
On Friday you don't have to worry
On Friday it's a good day
So you don't have to care.

Alice Whittaker (8)
Christ Church CE Primary School

Springtime

In spring, the weather is getting warm,
Birds singing in the trees.
Sunshine comes out
Flowers growing in the ground and
People everywhere, running around.

Craig Boughey (8)
Christ Church CE Primary School

The Hydra

The hydra snaps off your head
He loves it when you're dead,
He never stops drizzling
He's always grizzling
And this is what he said.
'I love it when I'm fed
In my very comfy bed.
So now you'll have to die,
Because I hate it when you lie.
Well I will eat you anyway,
Because we waited until May.
I'll eat you with my very sharp teeth,
With an extra little leaf,
My children are waiting,
So you best be ready for fainting
Are you going to cry?
Goodbye!'

Ryan Birkett (9)
Christ Church CE Primary School

What Is A Bully?

A bully is . . .
A fighting boxer
A mean machine,
A money stealer,
A feeling wrecker.
A name caller
A heart breaker,
A fat puncher
A hard walker.
A jealous coward!

Jake Stanton (11)
Christ Church CE Primary School

A Bully Is . . .

A bully is . . .
A friendship wrecker
A money stealer
A pusher, a shover
A jealous coward
A name caller
A horrible person.

Do you want to be a bully?
Think!

Laura Arnold (10)
Christ Church CE Primary School

Summer

I like summer when it's warm
Splashing in the sea when it's warm,
I like walking on the sand when it's warm.
Stamp, stamp, stamp, walking on the sand
When it's warm.
I like digging in the sand, dig, dig, dig.
Digging in the sand when it's warm.
I like summer. I do, I do!

Jordan Longdon (8)
Christ Church CE Primary School

Stop Bullying Poem

Bullying is naughty,
Bullying can frighten you.
Bullying can make you feel upset
Bullying can be bad
Bullying can make you feel sad.
Bullying is cruel
Bullying can harm you.

Charlotte Wiggin (10)
Christ Church CE Primary School

Spring

Spring is the best time because all
The pretty flowers grow.
All the leaves and beautiful birds come back.

I hear birds sing again,
I love all the trees, plants and birds.

Roses are red, violets are blue
Every day in spring,
I love so much too.

Jemma Ball (8)
Christ Church CE Primary School

Friends

F riends forever
R eal friends stick together
I f you fall out, it won't last
E verywhere I go Paige and Charlotte are there
N ever walk away
D on't push them away
S haring and loving for each other.

Demi Jeffrey (9)
Christ Church CE Primary School

Spring

S pring is when the flowers start to grow
P eople like to watch the flowers in bloom
R ight away, people like to see the birds singing
I n spring, it is very clean in houses
N ow grown-ups are happy
G irls and boys are happy as well.

Callum Cheatle (8)
Christ Church CE Primary School

The Sea Serpent

The ripples across the deep dark sea
At last, a sighting of the sea serpent.
It splashes and crashes in the distance,
In the distance, in the distance it lies.

This creature says beyond its eyes,
'Kill, death, blood, destroy, never live.'
You'll never escape when you are the eyes of his meal,
He will crush you and eat your flesh.

Humans dare not cross this sea,
Only a lad called Tiny Tim.
Poor boy he never broke free
No one ever saw Tiny Tim again.

Alice Jansen (9)
Christ Church CE Primary School

Cold Snow

The winter is nippy
You can play outdoors in the frosty snow
You slip and slide in the car.
The icicles are sharp so I would watch out.
The weather is cold in the winter
Turn on the heater, it's freezing in here!
The grass is crisp outside,
Snow, snow on my toe.
The snow smells fresh.
My toe is numb.
Snow, snow on my nose
It trickles down to my toes.
The snow is white.

Thomas Vigrass (7)
Christ Church CE Primary School

The Summer Sun

The summer sun is so summery,
Everyone wants to go to the beach.
The tickly sand tickles my feet.
Everybody needs something to eat - an ice cream.
I'm splashing in the water with my hands ,
My feet are cold and so is the sand.
It's not cold, the winds blow away.
I'll go in a boat and swim away
I want to come another day.
Then the sun just goes down,
The sky is blue
The clouds go by.
The sea is blue and
I say goodbye!

Danielle Murphy (7)
Christ Church CE Primary School

Friends

Friends are what people need
They share and give and tell
They never tell a lie
Friends are always helpful
They help you do your homework
And help you when you're down
Best friends don't call you names
And if they did, you would be upset
Boys and girls can get along
And can be friends, no matter
How many times people try
And make them fight.

Samantha Holmes (10)
Christ Church CE Primary School

Snow, Snow

Snow, snow, floating down to my toes,
Drifting down to the ground below.
Snow, snow, upon the ground
On the floor making a sound.
Crunch! Crunch! in the snow.
When you walk it glows and glows.

Snow, snow, dancing down from my nose
It shivers down to the bottom of my toes,
Snow, snow, in the sky
Flutters down as the clouds go by.

Jade Porter (8)
Christ Church CE Primary School

Summer

I like summer when it is burning
And I like the sea because
I like surfing.
I like summer when it's warm
But I hate prawns.
I like the sound of dripping ice cream
But I hate it when I have bad dreams
I like the summer beach with all the
Colourful shells
But I hate it when my sister
Throws pebbles.

Sophie Gunter (7)
Christ Church CE Primary School

The Sun

The sun is glowing on me
I feel how nice you are,
The sun is beautiful
I feel good in my heart.

Luke Antill (7)
Christ Church CE Primary School

Friendship

F riends are good to you
R eally help you if you're stuck
I n good and bad times, they're there for you
E xciting games we play
N ever go away from you
D on't get into trouble
S omeone you go to if you're in trouble
H appy people come to you
I will always be your friend
P lay in the park and have fun.

Joshua Gilbody (9)
Christ Church CE Primary School

Always Friends

F riends never break up, always
R eady to have a game of football.
I n school, we always play
E arly at school we stand together
N ever ever argue amongst ourselves
D epending if we are very sad or not.
S ad people are never happy friends
H aving a good laugh.
I f we always fight
P eople are never friends.

John Harris (10)
Christ Church CE Primary School

Spring

The birds are singing in the tree
Flowers showing
Time for bed
The sky is sunny.

Jack Marlow (8)
Christ Church CE Primary School

Friendship

F riends will never break up
R evising with each other
I n the class, friends work together
E veryone who are friends stick together
N ever get told off unless it is for your friend
D evastated if your friend leaves
S haring everything, including feelings
H opeful and happy when they do something nice
I never feel upset when I am with my friend
P als forever and never hurt each other.

Peter Allsop (10)
Christ Church CE Primary School

Spring Holiday

Spring, spring, drifting spring
I love the springtime
When the tree's leaves fall down
Spring is one of the loveliest seasons,
Bringing lots of joy to everyone
In different countries and of
Different ages to go.

Reece Caunt (7)
Christ Church CE Primary School

Rainbow

R ainbow glittering, glittering bright
A fter the rain, here comes the rainbow.
I ron colours, shining bright.
N othing more beautiful than the rainbow
B eauty shines all over the land.
O h dear! Oh dear! There goes the rainbow
W hat a wonderful time we had.

Michael Lawrence (8)
Cooper & Jordan Primary School

Snowflakes

S nowflakes fall from the sky
N ear to touching the ground
O n they whirl and whirl
W hen you hold them they begin to melt away
F alling, falling, twizzling, twirling
L eaping to touch the ground
A nxiously twizzling about
K icking, pushing, dancing
E verywhere falling and prancing
S now comes, snow falls.

Madeline Thorn (8)
Cooper & Jordan Primary School

Weather

W ind and rain swirling round and round,
E aster bunnies, bouncing up and down.
A utumn has been, it comes and goes,
T rees have fallen to my knees,
H air blowing in the breeze,
E arth going round and round,
R ain splashing slowly down, down, down!

Danielle Talbot (9)
Cooper & Jordan Primary School

Weather

W ind and rain and a hurricane
E vergreen trees and rain from the seas,
A sun that's burning the Earth is turning
T wo hurricanes and no more trains
H urrying down the lanes because of hurricanes
E qual amounts of rain as there was pain
R ain and rain, hurricane, hurricane.

Matthew Bryant (8)
Cooper & Jordan Primary School

Snowflakes

S nowflakes floating to the ground
N ow it's time to kick around
O n top of the branches, the snowflakes hang
W hirling, twirling and swirling
F aster and faster they fall
L akes frozen like an ice skating rink
A utumn gone, winter arrives
K nitted scarves keeping children warm
E veryone sledging on the hills
S nowflakes melting as the sun comes out.

Max Standerwick (8)
Cooper & Jordan Primary School

Weather

W hat is it going to be like today?
E veryone always asks
A re we going to be warm?
T hought not!
H ere comes the rain
E ngland can always be relied upon to
R ain!

David Rea-Gardner (9)
Cooper & Jordan Primary School

Rainbow

R ed is for the roses
A mber is for the shine of the lights
I ndigo is for the violets
N avy is for the never-ending colour
B lue is for the sky
O range is for the sun
W hite is for the clouds that the rainbow sits upon.

Holly Sheldon (9)
Cooper & Jordan Primary School

Snowflakes

S is for the snow which drops from the sky
N ice and pretty
O ne at a time,
W et on our faces,
F luttering around
L ively and twirling
A lways in the wind.
K issing my nose
E ven my toes.
S hould I be barefoot?

Andrew Munns (9)
Cooper & Jordan Primary School

Twister

T rees destroyed
W ind blowing people
I see it coming
S ave the animals
T elephone lines down
E veryone hiding
R ubble now covers the town.

George Morgan (8)
Cooper & Jordan Primary School

Sunny

S unshine is my favourite weather
U mbrellas don't need them ever
N o winter coat to keep you warm
N o nasty rain or windy storm
Y ellow sunshine - I love you!

Olivia Moseley (8)
Cooper & Jordan Primary School

Snowflakes

S now is falling, flowing down,
N ow to build a snowman.
O n his way is Santa
W ith all the presents in his sack.
F lakes of snow landing on the bobble on his hat
L akes are frozen solid,
A fter it's a thick, white town
K ids are playing in the snow.
E veryone is having fun
S now is falling, flowing down.

Sam Jones (8)
Cooper & Jordan Primary School

Raining

R ivers flowing all the same way
A lways raining, every day
I like to run, jump and splash
N oisy rain, wind and lash
I ndoors is the best when it rains
N eed the Council, we've got blocked drains
G oing now - I'm very wet!

Bradley Matthews (8)
Cooper & Jordan Primary School

Twister

T error in any town
W ill lead people down
I think it should go away
S hould it not, I won't stay
T wister comes hard and fast
E ventually it won't last
R ubble, we pray is a thing of the past.

Matthew Kirby (9)
Cooper & Jordan Primary School

Snowflakes

S himmering, shining, falling to the ground,
N ever-ever stopping twirling, whirling round,
O n the pavement in the street
W hirling this way twirling that
F alling, falling, falling to the ground
L ittle ones, big ones, all different sizes,
A ll shimmering and shining
K eeps me cold
E ver white, ever cold
S nowing again.

Bethany Jones (8)
Cooper & Jordan Primary School

Frosty

F reezing the grass to white,
R ushing onto the slippery, sharp ice,
O ver the rivers and lakes it crisply freezes,
S napping like glass, crackling under shoes, snap, snap!
T he air is chilly, the day is cold,
Y ou know Jack Frost is at work again!

Joshua Wilson (8)
Cooper & Jordan Primary School

Stormy

S creaming, whistling, howling wind,
T hrashing rain hurling against my face,
O ver the houses, lightning flashes,
R ichocheting thunder rebounds around me,
M onstrous puddles flooding the ground,
Y elling children dashing for shelter.

Eliott Cook (8)
Cooper & Jordan Primary School

Hailstones

H ailstones make a horrible sound
A nd frightened birds scatter
I ce takes over the lakes
L ots of hailstones. Bash! Bash!
S mash! Bash! Was that the window?
T ons of hailstones dropping on the ground,
O ne by one denting the cars
N o one goes outside
E ach hailstone settles on the ground
S oon the storm is over.

Amy Hawes (8)
Cooper & Jordan Primary School

Snowball

S nowy white ground all around,
N othing looks the same,
O ur hands are cold,
W hen the icy wind blows,
B etter put on our gloves to hold the snow,
A ll the children playing,
L ook at them go, look at them throw,
L aughing, shouting, running in the snow.

Rebecca Garbett (9)
Cooper & Jordan Primary School

Weather

W inter's coming,
E ast winds can bring snow,
A utumn is ending,
T his we know.
H aunting the
E arth and
R emembering the glow of summer.

Thomas Fielder (9)
Cooper & Jordan Primary School

Snowflakes

S nowflakes falling quickly from the sky,
N ewly coated fields,
O f deep thick snow,
W hirling, twirling, swirling,
F rosty and glistening,
L ying softly on the ground,
A ll around snow is seated,
K eeping pure whiteness
E very flake individual,
S wirling, twirling, whirling.

Jessica Green (9)
Cooper & Jordan Primary School

Raining

R ags are wet,
A nd puddles are flowing,
I n my bedroom
N o sun
I s out
N o good reason to go in the
G arden at all.

Samuel Cole (8)
Cooper & Jordan Primary School

Rainbow

R aining
A nd play splash! Splash!
I n the puddles
N ow I'm wet, wet, wet!
B lowing, blowing the wind is blowing,
O n the trees, the leaves are falling,
W inter weather isn't nice.

Megan Hughes (8)
Cooper & Jordan Primary School

Thunderstorm

T hrashing against the sky,
H urdling and cracking all the trees,
U pstairs you might be asleep,
N ow come loud *bangs!*
D rums beating, faster and faster,
E verywhere it hits you on your body,
R aining, raining, raining,
S tuck in the brown mud,
T ill you get mucky and wet,
O r scaring the life out of you,
R oaring like a lion,
M ore, more . . . go yellow thunder, go!

Reece Lewis (8)
Cooper & Jordan Primary School

Snowflakes

S nowy grounds all around,
N othing on the floor but a blanket of white,
O ver the fields nothing in sight but
W hite, white, white.
F aster and faster it starts to fall,
L aughing children play in the snow,
A ll the children excited and throwing snowballs,
K aleidoscope patterns in each flake,
E very rooftop and tree covered,
S oft and silent snowflakes watch them fall.

Jamie Evans (9)
Cooper & Jordan Primary School

Snowflakes

S hivering in a snowstorm,
N ight sky lit up by snowflakes,
O wls hooting in the night sky,
W indows banging,
F reezing weather outside,
L akes frozen, starting to break,
A nd thousands of snowmen outside,
K ing-size snowflakes,
E ight o'clock snow stops,
S nowflakes glittering in the night sky.

Lauren Hanslow (8)
Cooper & Jordan Primary School

Weather

W ind and rain splish! Splash! Splosh!
E ver and ever the rain goes on,
A nd at last the rain has gone,
T hen we can go and play.
H aving lots of fun running here and there,
E very time we play it begins to rain,
R ain, rain, rain, splish! Splash! Splosh!

Jacob Marklew (8)
Cooper & Jordan Primary School

Spring

Spring is a lovely sight,
Every day is always bright,
All the animals being born,
All the frogs growing spawn,
Butterflies and bees swirling round,
Baby lambs safe and sound,
Lovely flowers start to bloom,
Spring will be here very soon.

Hannah Whittle (10)
Curdworth Primary School

Roger Rabbit

Roger Rabbit pranced about
Buggzy said 'You're rather stout'
'I think not pal, I'd know for sure
Betty would find you such a bore'
Roger stormed off from the scene
Thinking Buggzy very mean
Down to the pub to meet some mates
Hoping Betty be his date
On the stroke of midnight Roger said,
'Betty you look great in red'
Roger knew just what to do
He did something quite ascue
One quick peck on Betty's cheek
Left her feeling very weak
She threw their ring straight into the bin
Poor old Roger felt terribly dim
Next month he fell for Betty's sister
He tried to tell her of his blister
She laughed aloud at Roger's blister
Whilst he tried to grab and kiss her
She was the sort who liked a joke
Together with a diet Coke
They had a very pleasant marriage
In a super golden carriage.

Joe McKenna (10)
Curdworth Primary School

Friends Are There

Friends are always there,
Just like apples and pears,
A good friend will listen,
And not go to prison.

Whatever the weather,
You'll be best friends forever,
Whether you like or hate them.

Some have more friends than others,
Some just have their brothers,
Many are in groups
And let you borrow their hula hoops.

Whatever the weather,
You'll be best friends forever,
Whether you like or hate them.

A friend that is right,
Will never ever fight,
Someone who will care,
Is very, very rare.

Whatever the weather,
You'll be best friends forever,
Whether you like or hate them.

Freisha Patel (10)
Curdworth Primary School

Family And Friends

I like pets
My friend likes football
My mom likes cooking
And my dad's really tall
My cousin always falls
But now I like holidays
And my friend likes pets
My dad likes my mom
My mom likes my dad
My cousin likes my dog
My best friend likes me
I like my best friends
Jake likes Charles
Charles likes me
Jake likes me
Jake, me and Charles like football
Robert likes to build
Holly likes writing poems
Beth likes playing
Chris likes crisps
Aaron likes quads
Sam likes reading
Charles likes eating
Jon likes talking
Jamie likes Jack
Peter likes swimming, so does Ben
Rhys likes computers
I like Mrs Taylor
Now you know people
We have different likes but
We all like our teacher!

Tom Powell (10)
Curdworth Primary School

Space

Big planets roll,
The sky's black as coal,
We see stars in the past,
We've got there at last,
Space!

Rockets fly through
Some think it's not true,
Is there any more life?
The cold's sharp as a knife,
Space!

There's much fascination,
From every nation,
We all want to go there,
At it we all stare,
Space!

The sun is so hot,
Big rocks, there's a lot,
It takes time to arrive,
You can't stay alive,
Space!

There is such wonder,
And many a blunder,
Connected with space,
Of life there's no trace.
Space!

Sam Rhodes (10)
Curdworth Primary School

Is A Bike Any Good Without A Bell?

Is a bike any good without a bell?
If I didn't have one I'd have to yell.
'Get out the way,'
I would say,
As I dodged obstacles throughout the day.
Tap-dancing tomatoes and a gymnastic cream cake,
Imagine the mess I would make.
I'd have to wear protective wellies,
To protect myself from mutant jellies.
A bell would be good,
But much to my fears,
I realise that jellies
Don't have ears.

Lucy Fisher (10)
Curdworth Primary School

Summer

The sun gazes in our eyes
Flowers bloom in wonderful colours
Birds tweet their morning song
Grass sparkles in the day
Lambs skip to the bird's tune
Boys are playing tag
Dogs chase the cats
Mice jump at the cheese
Butterflies fly with delight
Children play in the paddling pools
That's how summer goes.

Rhys Yates (11)
Curdworth Primary School

Favourite Things

I like pink, purple and blue,
Yellow, green and orange too,
I like pizza, bacon and chips,
Especially Doritos with barbecue dips.
I like Jade, Freisha and Holly
Also Abi, and of course Molly.
I like summer with the bright yellow sun
Me and my friends have heaps of fun.
I like bluebells, tulips and heathers,
They feel so soft and as light as feathers,
I'll love these things forever and ever,
But I'll love them more when they're all together.

Stephanie Downes (11)
Curdworth Primary School

Art

Art is my favourite thing to do
Orange, red, yellow and blue,
Painting and drawing and colouring too,
I like to make models out of clay and
Paint them colours like red, gold and grey,
I especially like to draw things that are blue like
The ocean and clouds and swimming pools too,
Paint brushes, pencils, paint and glue,
Art is the thing I always want to do.

Nitesh Chamdal (10)
Curdworth Primary School

A Teddy Bear

A teddy bear,
Is round and chubby,
A teddy bear has a great big tummy,
He eats a lot 24/7,
He likes to play all day and night,
He enjoys football and rugby too,
The teddy bear has a cute face,
His eyes are small and so, so dark,
By the way his name is Spark!

Jake Gallagher (11)
Curdworth Primary School

Friends

In life you'll make a few good friends
It's on these friends you can depend
They will lend a hand and always understand
Tell you the truth, never ask for proof
Be at your side in ups and downs
Know when to shout and not to make a sound
To sing and laugh with, to reach the stars with
Look after your friends and they will be with
You till the end.

Rebecca Woodward (10)
Curdworth Primary School

What A Horrible Class!

Lucy's friends with Abi,
But not friends with Rachel,
Rachel's friends with Nicole,
But not friends with Amber,
Amber's friends with Jenny,
But not friends with Steph,
What a horrible class!

Steph's friends with Holly,
But not friends with Lucy,
Lucy's friends with Jade,
But not friends with Katie,
Katie's friends with Freisha,
But not friends with Nicole,
What a horrible class!

Nicole's friends with Jenny,
But not friends with Heather,
Heather's friends with Abi,
But not friends with Hannah,
Hannah's friends with Rebecca,
But not friends with Jade,
What a horrible class!

Our teacher's always saying:
'What a horrible class!'

Lucy Foster (11)
Curdworth Primary School

Flowers

Roses from Russia and
Daisies from Denmark
Pansies from Poland and
Lilies from London.

Bluebells from Brighton,
Snowdrops from Scotland,
Nettles from Norway and
Foxgloves from France.

Those are a few of our favourite plants!

Charlotte Lacey (10)
Curdworth Primary School

Dreams

Dream a dream of happiness
Flowers that smell like perfume
Chocolate that tastes so delicious
And all different flavoured ice cream
A holiday, out on the beach
Now that's a wonderful dream!

Dream a dream of sadness
When tears come to your eyes
When wars are going on,
The sound of guns shooting animals
The many injuries and deaths
Now that's a terrible dream!

Dream a dream of horror
Ghosts and monsters chase
Sometimes you appear in a graveyard
And are under the ground
Sometimes you are in a haunted house
With creepy windows and doors
Now that's a scary dream!

Emily Cope (10)
Fairhaven Primary School

The Dream Theatre

I'm in the queue with my ticket
I'm going in . . . *wow*
It's huge!
I just stand there with my mouth wide open.
I had some sweets in my hand when I came in
Where are they now?
They're on the floor, I pick them up.
Oh no, the show's starting, lights are flashing, people singing.
'Joseph, Joseph is it really you?' they sing.
Quickly get into our seats,
We are sitting right at the front,
The show's brilliant!
The show's about to have a break.
'We are terribly sorry, but one of our actors is very ill!
We need a little girl who can sing and dance!' said a man.
I jump up and say 'I can sing and dance!'
I am up on stage singing the last song,
Now I'm finally finished.
' . . . Jessica . . . Jessica . . . wake up!'
'Morning, Mum I've just had the most brilliant dream.
It was about my dream theatre.'
And we are going to the theatre later,
I wonder if it's the same as I dreamt?

Jessica Knott-Packwood (10)
Fairhaven Primary School

Moonlight Fly

The moon shone through the trees at night,
The stars were like lights in the sky,
Footsteps echo through the forest,
Birds awake.
I'm taken off my feet into the air, by birds as soft as silk,
The moon looks like a golf ball floating in space.
The birds swooped down and drop me off,
What a ride that was.

Joshua Pagett (10)
Fairhaven Primary School

Fairy Dust

Through the swirling, twirling snow
The fairy dust starts to fall
The children start to run outside
To play with all the snow
They start to build a snowman
With eyes, mouth, hat and nose
They put a scarf and buttons
On the nice soft snow,
When they had finished
Something amazing happened
He started to come alive
Playing in the snow
Making butterflies
I don't know how it happened
It must have been that fairy dust
But how I don't know!

Emily Hill (10)
Fairhaven Primary School

I Read A Poem!

I read a poem only last night,
The words were wearied,
They didn't seem right,
The princess was ugly up till the end,
I think the prince was right round the bend,
The flowers were candy,
The drinks were all goo,
People were staring at me and at . . . y*ou!*

Alice Mason (10)
Fairhaven Primary School

The Lion

Antelope running from a beast with dragons' teeth,
A magnificent monster, with a mane made of gold,
The prey is tiring, here's the chance,
The antelope looks up, frozen in time,
The trembling creature daren't use his horns,
For the beast's skin is as thick as leather,
In the blink of an eye he seems to grow,
The amber eyes, pits of fury,
His proud, silky coat glinting in the sun ,
Silently, he glides towards victim,
And sinks his teeth into the antelope's dying heart,
Deadly silence hits Africa and then a thud,
No blood stains the grass, there's no wound to be seen,
Just the old antelope and the lion,
The golden beast, unseen to the human eye.

Lucy Rogers (10)
Fairhaven Primary School

Disco Dancer

Dancing round and round
Hearing all the sounds
Moving to the beat
Don't want to sit,
Keeping to the groove
Swirling round and round
Still hearing those sounds
I can't stop, gotta
Keep movin' to the music
The moves are great
Gotta keep movin'
But now I stop!

Georgia Kirkham (10)
Fairhaven Primary School

The Stripy Tiger

The stripy tiger,
Had sharp, razor blade teeth,
Eyes like balls of fire,
Stripes so colourful and bright,
A body as long as a table,
Legs as long as a stick,
Then the tiger saw something,
It was beautiful,
It was a flamingo.

Charlotte McEvoy (10)
Fairhaven Primary School

My Family

In my family mum is a big fluffy pillow,
My mum's yellow as the sun, so warm and cuddly,
She's a bumblebee,
Mum is the sun, hot and warm,
She is a white soft top,
My mum is a bed, cosy and snugly,
She is 'Changing Rooms'
My mum is a lobster that's bright red.

My dad is a car
He's a blue and green
Dad is a dog, strong and long
A meal of chicken
Dad is 'Robot Wars'
He is ripped jeans
My dad is a rainbow
A soft sofa.

Justine Belcher (9)
Four Oaks Junior School

My Family

In my family
My dad is blue, sometimes jolly,
Sometimes cross,
He is a horse, cheerful and patient,
He is rain, happy and energetic,
He's a hat always falling off people's heads,
He's a cushion bouncing onto the floor,
He is an athlete running the London Marathon,
He is a Chinese takeaway, delicious and tender.

My hamster is ginger, happy and bright,
He is a pop star, flashy and sparky,
He is a bright summer's day,
He's a shoe fast and quick,
He's a lilo,
He is 'Grease Lightning'
He's chicken nuggets.

Samuel Commander (9)
Four Oaks Junior School

My Family

In my family, my dad is a big comfy armchair
Which I fall asleep on and his arm is like a pillow.
He is the colour of the sky when it is bright blue,
My dad is always bright like the sun on a nice day,
My dad is a dog who plays in the park with us,
My dad is a bowl of spaghetti which I could eat really fast,
My dad is the news,
My dad is a soft white top.

My mom is a bright yellow sun which is yellow,
My mom is lasagne which I could eat in seconds,
My mom is 'Fat Friends'
My mom is a lovely pillow,
My mom is a pair of designer jeans.

Gemma Smith (8)
Four Oaks Junior School

My Family's Ups And Downs

In my family my mum is a lilac-purple,
She's the flower in my garden,
She's a dog without a bark,
She's the sun killing the rain,
She's a dress from River Island,
She's a chair with bags of class,
She's 'The Simpsons' just like Marge,
She's spag bol the best of all.

My dad is the colour black,
He's a wolf with a shivering howl,
He's the thunder in the sky,
He's a shirt that's screaming 'No'
He's a rocking chair that's squeaky,
He's the news on channel 5,
He's coleslaw on my plate, yuck,
And that's my family!

Georgina Woodward (8)
Four Oaks Junior School

My Family

In my family my mom is
The colour of pink, like candyfloss,
She is a sunny day,
She is like a woolly hat on a winter's day,
She is a dog running around the house,
She is a comfy, soft beanbag,
She is 'Changing Rooms'
She is a warm bowl of custard.

My dad is the colour blue,
He is a hamster,
He is a rain cloud in the sky,
He is a dark, black cloak,
He is an old, rusty, brown chair,
He is a giant bowl of cornflakes.

Elizabeth McNab (9)
Four Oaks Junior School

My Family

In my family . . .
Mum is
A colour of blue just like the midnight sky,
She is a guinea pig,
She is a sunny day shining, so bright,
An armchair, so warm and soft,
She is 'EastEnders'
A plate of spaghetti, so stringy and delicate,
A pile of knitted jumpers, so warm and soft.

My dad is . . .
The colour red, so bright and sunny,
A piece of furniture like a sofa,
He's the weather, spring so fresh and nice,
A meal of sausages, so soft and chewy,
The TV programme 'Like Car Sharks'.

Simone Gerald (8)
Four Oaks Junior School

My Family

In my family . . .
My mum is bright yellow
She is like a cat when she is nice
My mum is the sun, bright and warm
My mum is a jumper, cosy and firm
She is a settee, really soft
She is 'Coronation Street'
She is a piece of sponge cake.

In my family . . .
My dad is light blue
He is a rhino, strong and powerful
He is a light blue day where the sky is clear
He is like a leather coat, strong and tough.

Hannah Skelding (9)
Four Oaks Junior School

My Family

In my family my brother is three Shredded Wheat,
He is dark blue
He is thunder in the sky
He is a fierce bull
He is a plate of beans on toast
He is a scruffy pile of clothes
He is an unmade bed.

My mum is yellow
She is a sparkling star in the sky
She is a lovely collie dog
She is a neat pile of clothes
She is a soft and cuddly teddy
She is a cooking programme
She is a lovely salad.

My dad is amazing
He is like black magic
He is a wild horse in a field
He is a slightly-creased pile of clothes
He is a dark cloud in the sky
He is a joker
He is chicken nuggets and chips.

Greg Mansell (8)
Four Oaks Junior School

Why School!

I hate having to go to school,
Every holiday that is the rule,
At school I hardly get to play,
My teachers will always say,
Now tidy up my desk,
It always gets messed,
At a table munching food at lunch,
There was always this huge horrible crunch.

Emma Biles (8)
Four Oaks Junior School

My Mad Family!

My brother is dark blue
He is a dog
He is a sunny day
He is a neat pile of jumpers.

He is a scruffy old chair
He is 'Power Rangers' with force
He is a plate full of chips.

My mum is sky-blue
My mum is a fluffy rabbit
She is a snowy night
My mum is a glittery dress
She is a brand new leather sofa
My mum is 'Hollyoaks'
She is a bowl of soup.
And that is my mad family!

Emily Heatherley (8)
Four Oaks Junior School

Limericks

Lizard fever
I see something lying about, it's a lizard,
It is far too hot for a blizzard,
It has long jaws,
Just as long claws,
He is such a furious lizard.

Lion bites
I see a lion's wide round mane
He is the king of the jungle with its fame
It has long claws
Just like long jaws
It is not very heavy when it rains.

Matthew Watts (9)
Four Oaks Junior School

My Fandabydosy Family

My brother is . . .
A warm, comforting pink who's always there for me,
A dog that's always on the move,
A sunny morning on a brand new day,
A scruffy, torn T-shirt that hasn't been washed,
A soft, comfy sofa in front of the TV,
A cartoon off Cartoon Network,
And a yummy pizza that everyone likes.
That's my bro!

My mum is . . .
A cuddly pink,
A busy bee,
A warm rainbow,
A neat pile of Pjs,
A warm bed,
'Coronation Street'
And a sponge pudding warm as can be,
That's my mum!

My dad is . . .
A cheerful red,
A scurrying hamster all over the place,
The sun at noon,
A neat drawer of socks,
A nice armchair,
A programme of 'The Bill'
And a roast turkey
That's my dad!

Matthew Goodall (9)
Four Oaks Junior School

School

(Based on 'Please Mrs Butler' by Allan Alhberg)

'George what's the matter?'
'I've torn my page in half,
I've spilt my ink,
I've lost my rubber miss,
What shall I do?'
'Run a thousand miles
Go and work on the roof
Do what you want my flower, but don't bother me
George what's the matter now?'
'I've put a crack in my desk
I've lost my pen
What shall I do?'
'Hide under the table
Sail away to sea
Do what you want my love, but don't bother me.
George what is the matter now?'
'I've lost my pencil case
I need the loo,
I've fell off my chair miss,
What shall I do?'
'Lock yourself in your locker
Run home if you want
But don't bother *me!*'

Oliver Smith (9)
Four Oaks Junior School

Ponies

My pony has lots of riding lessons
It has four lessons a week
She can jump very high
Every day it canters very fast
I have to clean her stable
Every single day.

She is as beautiful as a queen
As happy as a smile
I always brush my beautiful pony
And I always give her its favourite food
Every single day.

She is very, very sporty,
And very, very powerful
She loves to play games
And canter in the field
Every single day.

Rosie Wilkes (8)
Four Oaks Junior School

School Days

Monday mornings always boring,
Teachers mostly always snoring,
Mum leaves me at the gate,
I run over to my mate.
I've forgotten how to use my pencil,
Is it best to use my stencil?
I don't want to play that game,
I think that it's very lame.
Children running in the playground,
Silence! and there was no sound,
I hate the only rule,
I want to be in another school.

Nicole Alexandra Parsons (8)
Four Oaks Junior School

As A Crocodile

As a crocodile attacks
With its horrible teeth
It takes you down
To the bottom of the river and kills you
Then later it comes and chews you.

When it comes to eat you
It has very scaly skin
It opens its mouth
Its teeth dig into you
It eats you in a blink.

As a crocodile hears
He will pop up with his claws
At the ready
It is very mad
If nothing is there.

Harry Emberson
Four Oaks Junior School

Teachers Get Mad

'Please Mrs Bennett this boy Louie Blue
Has snapped my pencil miss what shall I do?'
'Grip it tight, hide it away,
Why would he want it anyway?'
'Please Mr Martin this boy Louie Blue,
He's taken my rubber sir what shall I do?'
'Ask him for it back!
Take it out of his drawer,
Don't ask me again dear or I am
Going to roar!'

Cameron Edkins (9)
Four Oaks Junior School

I See A Siberian Tiger

I see a Siberian tiger
Walking amongst the tall pine trees,
With its eyes that blaze green.
Power starts as it starts to move
Further into the wood,
Towards a big thicket.
Whilst a dozen birds fly out of their comfy nests,
A small group of deer run out of the woods,
The tiger runs out of the thicket
And takes its moment of pride.

The group of deer circle around their young
As the tiger circles, looking for a victim.
Suddenly its eyes widen and it pounces.
It strikes and sinks its claws into the victim.
Easy meal!

William Richards (8)
Four Oaks Junior School

Lizard/Snake

Lizard
There was a big grey lizard,
Who's enjoying the heat, not a blizzard,
Great long claws,
Like snapping jaws,
What a happy grey, old lizard.

Sssnake
There was once a great snake,
Who slithered into the lake,
He turned blue,
Got the flu,
To cure it he ate a cream cake.

Harry James John Eady (9)
Four Oaks Junior School

What Shall I Do Miss?

'I have a pencil that keeps snapping Miss,
What shall I do?'
'Get a new one, get a pen,
Do whatever you think.'
'The table that I sit at it keeps falling apart Miss,
What shall I do?'
'Do it on the floor, do it on the roof,
Do whatever you think.'
'The school gate keeps locking Miss,
What shall I do?'
'Climb over the wall, bash it down,
Do whatever you think.'

'You know our school display Miss,
It keeps falling down,
What shall I do?'
'Staple it to the wall, hold it up yourself
Do whatever you think.'
'I have this ruler Miss, it keeps snapping,
What shall I do?'
'Coat it with metal, don't sit on it,
Do whatever you think.'

Danny Nicoll (8)
Four Oaks Junior School

My Kitty

Kitty cute, paused beside the fire,
Up in the tree she climbs higher and higher,
Every day she's terribly funny,
And loves a good rub on her furry tummy.

Chloe Josephine Swadkin (9)
Four Oaks Junior School

The Teenager

The teenager, a foul beast,
Where they come from no one knows.
Some believe they come from the centre of Earth,
With a spot on the end of their nose.

Their communication is something strange,
All they do is grunt and groan.
When parents try to wake them,
They just roll over with a moan.

They stay up all night,
Waking others in bed.
When they hear the word 'sleep',
Their heart fills with dread.

Whenever you see them,
They're up to no good.
They've never done right,
They never could.

So, whenever you see a teen,
Don't stand and stay.
Just turn around
And run, run away.

Elliot George Cotterill (11)
Four Oaks Junior School

I See A Tiger . . .

I see a tiger hunting down its prey,
Crouching down in the long grass,
It's walking around its prey,
Getting ready to pounce and spring
It is a handsome thing.

Luke Woodward (9)
Four Oaks Junior School

My Family

In my family . . .
Alex is a pitch-black night
He's a wild dog who bites everyone
He's a terrible thunderstorm
He is a ripped shirt in the back of the drawer
He's a solid chair as hard as a rock
He is 'Midsommer Murders'
He's a rotten bowl of custard.

In my family . . .
Mum is a yellow sun
She is a lovely ginger cat
She is a sunny day in the fields
She is a pretty red dress
She is a comfy sofa
She is 'Home and Away'
She is a lovely cooked dinner.

Jack Cartwright (8)
Four Oaks Junior School

Cats!

I see a cub as playful as can be,
I stare at the cub and it smiles at me,
Its spotty mum comes around,
With the food, that she has found,
There is its father, the one with a mane,
Here it comes running, you can see the strain,
Look at its parents around the cub,
There is the child who wants a big rub.

Antonia Mander (8)
Four Oaks Junior School

To Write A Poem

(Based on 'Through That Door' by John Cotton)

Through that door,
Is an enchanted fire,
Where flames dance,
And sparks prance,
Where wood burns,
And paper turns,
With a blazing fright,
And an amazing sight.

Through that door,
Is a magical garden,
Where violets bloom,
And daisies have room,
Where dreams fly,
And animals lie,
With lots of growing flowers,
You'll be there for hours.

Alex Duffy (10)
Four Oaks Junior School

Mad Monday Mornings

'Miss I haven't learnt my spellings,
Where's my ruler Miss,
I've lost my pencil Miss,
Miss I haven't got a book,
How do you do this?
I left my tuck at home Miss,
Miss, I've lost my pen,
Where's my PE kit Miss?
I didn't bring my pencil case Miss,
Miss where's my uniform?
Where's the dictionary Miss?
I've lost my shoe Miss,
Miss, yesterday I got kidnapped by a robot,
I've lost my mind Miss!'

Natalie Parkman (8)
Four Oaks Junior School

To Write A Poem

(Based on 'Through That Door' by John Cotton)

Through that door,
Is the haunted mansion,
Where spirits and souls lie,
And where no one has lived for years,
Where winter has come to the world,
And where ghosts and ghouls come out to play,
Spiders webs will glint in the moonlight,
Where stars light up the sky.

Through that door,
Is an enchanted garden,
Where flower after flower bloom,
And where spring comes to the world once more,
Where trees grow their leaves,
And where the sun shines for hours on end,
Where days grow long,
And the air is becoming warmer.

Katie Hearnden (10)
Four Oaks Junior School

Sky

I have a confusing channel called Sky,
I don't really know why,
Then my telly broke,
I started to choke,
I wish my telly could fly.

I have some games on TV,
Like swimming in the sea,
I am very good at that,
Like my friend Matt,
I wish there were more games for me.

Connor McElroy (8)
Four Oaks Junior School

To Write A Poem

(Based on 'Through That Door' by John Cotton)

Through that door,
Is an enchanted castle,
Where knights stand waiting for battle,
And dragons charge while knights stand and wait, wait,
Where will the dragons lay?
As they will be slaughtered by knights,
But the people realise that the dragons are enchanted,
While the time goes on the knights start to
Drift away while the dragons slay.

Through that door,
Is a damp cold cave,
Where a monster lies awake waiting for somebody to disturb him,
And when the monster is disturbed he gobbles them up in one gulp,
Whereabouts does he lay? Nobody knows,
In that cave where nobody goes, is a monster.

Eden Hyland (9)
Four Oaks Junior School

Lizard Life

There was a lizard eating a scrap of meat,
In the shade trying to keep away from the heat,
Now crouching down on the ground,
Like a cat ready to pound,
When it's quiet you can hear its heartbeat.

Lion
I see a lion with a big mane,
Running around a big dry plain,
Chasing a gazelle,
In grass coloured like a bell,
Everybody knows it definitely is not tame.

Aaron Dhadli (8)
Four Oaks Junior School

The Seasons

Spring is the time of year,
When fresh water springs flow crystal clear,
Blue tits and swallows soar through the sky,
While baby sparrows learn to fly.

Summer sun, golden and bright,
Shines through the window and gives us light,
With cloudless skies and windless air,
You can play in the garden without a care.

Autumn time and the trees are bare,
For leaves are floating through the air,
Raindrops are splattering, drip, drip, drop,
Fireworks in the distance go whirr and pop.

Winter has its many joys,
Like Christmas when you get new toys,
Every parcel is tied up with bows,
And if you're lucky it even snows.

Rachel Parkman (11)
Four Oaks Junior School

My Family Said

My mum said that I am a scientist,
My dad said that I am a palaeontologist,
My sister said it too,
My brother says that's true!

My grandad said that I am a surfer,
My nanny said that I am a burper,
My cousins said it too,
My family says that's true!

Liam Haigh (9)
Four Oaks Junior School

To Write A Poem

(Based on 'Through That Door' by John Cotton)

Through that door,
Is a bewildered sunken ship,
Where fishes wander like lost skeletons,
And a special somewhere for a divers descent,
Where baby fish swim all day,
In a winter wonderland far away,
Be that living human being,
Wandering all day in a funny sort of way.

Through that door,
Is a lonely battlefield in 1914,
Where homeless bodies still are yet to be removed,
And where living creatures loom all day,
Where left rotting bodies haunt you on your way,
Children cannot laugh under the black sky,
Villages have nothing to be jubilant about,
Their feelings full of dismay.

Through that door,
Is a creaky, crooked slimy cellar,
Where you resist to go,
And its feeling wash over you,
Where or when you're in trouble,
You have faith in your older brother,
With his eyes brown,
He'll save you once again!

Robert Slann (10)
Four Oaks Junior School

To Write A Poem

(Based on 'Through the Door' by John Cotton)

Through that door,
Is an enchanted garden,
Where the fairies live,
And the flowers grow,
Where pixies eat, drink and sleep,
No one goes in or ever comes out,
I wouldn't go in if I were you,
That's what's through that door.

Through that door,
Are the oceans' waves,
Where the treasure chest sits,
And the fish and sharks surround it,
Where the octopus guards it for the Ocean King,
You can see the crabs dancing on the rocks,
The mermaids singing through their shells,
That's what's through that door.

Through that door,
Is a palace of fun,
Where chocolate grows on trees,
And money falls from the sky,
Where the flowers bloom all alone,
The animals are happy and free,
You can see everybody enjoying themselves,
That's what's through that door.

Isabella Barber (10)
Four Oaks Junior School

To Write A Poem
(Based on 'Through That Door' by John Cotton)

Through that door,
Is the oceans waves,
Where fishes roam,
And sharks roar,
Where mermaids sing,
And crabs dance,
Where starfish play about,
Is this a dream?

Through that door,
Is a magical palace.
Where clocks and cups are alive,
And gardens are a plate of green.
Where the sun shines daily,
And princes and princesses meet,
And fall in love,
Why can't everywhere be like this?

Through that door,
Is a land of fairies,
Where centipedes teach,
And ants make houses,
Where flowers are sweet,
And spiders crawl,
What more could you want,
Than this magical land?

Erica Powell (10)
Four Oaks Junior School

To Write A Poem

(Based on 'Through That Door' by John Cotton)

Through that door,
Is a hideous beast,
Where he is waiting cos you are the feast,
And where he will lie,
Where you will scream and die,
Thou must not fear,
Cos your saviour is near,
All of it lies through that door.

Through that door,
Is the place of your dreams,
Where thunder hides and sunlight beams,
And where heavens will lie,
Where you must die,
That is where you will go,
A place that you know,
All of it lies through that door.

Through that door,
Is the Pacific Sea,
Where you are waiting for me,
And a place to give,
Where thou will live,
You do not know,
When will it show?
All of it lies through that door.

Charlie Hughes (10)
Four Oaks Junior School

To Write A Poem

(Based on 'Through That Door' by John Cotton)

Through that door,
Is a crumbling castle,
Where people go in and never come out,
And the castle is shaking and could fall down,
Where a dragon lives and he kills everyone in his way,
In the night the dragon sneaks around,
As he tries to get out of the castle door.

Through that door,
Is the ocean's waves,
Where the seas crash against the rocks,
And the shells sparkle against the sunlight,
Where sea animals are having really good fun,
Octopuses hiding under the caves,
The fishes hiding from their enemy sharks,
And when the starfish are resting and move slowly.

Through that door,
Is an enchanted garden,
Where plants and vegetables grow,
And green grass grows too in the sunshine,
Where you lie on your beds and relax until dawn,
And sit in your garden and let the fruit of the trees grow,
When you plant a seed you watch it develop,
And the flowers are sweets to eat for your tea.

George Howells (9)
Four Oaks Junior School

Through That Door

(Based on 'Through That Door' by John Cotton)

Through that door
Is a swooshing sea
Where fish roam
And crabs you'll see.
Where sharks creep up
Then catch the fish
And serve them
On a bloodstained dish.

Through that door
Is a fairy land,
Where pixies fly
And elves land,
Where you can find
The Easter bunny,
Or a magical bee
Making honey.

Through that door
Is a haunted house
Where *everything* is scared,
And the boldest mouse!
Where monsters loom
And vampires lie,
Waiting for a victim
Where on the spot, they'll die!

Ben Tipson (9)
Four Oaks Junior School

The Fox

The fiery fox, a living furnace,
Is hungry,
In the farmyard, he's bold, he's cold, he's sly.

Swiftly, he marches through the woods,
Gliding, blissfully,
A wild dash for food.

With a bushy, feathery tail, hanging like a rope,
Reaching out behind him, catching any moving prey,
He turns to pounce,
Leaping on a mouse,
With a downpour of satisfaction.

He burrows into the night sky,
Leaving emptiness behind him.

Michael Hogg (11)
Four Oaks Junior School

Who Am I?

He is a spiky-haired yellow demon,
Relentlessly gnawing into all that is good and true,
Funny yet naughty,
On a red summer's night,
A squishee drinking shark,
He is a plate of burning fire,
A trigger of a gun,
A spiky daredevil,
He is a heavy metal lovin' child,
A devil disguised as an angel,
An extreme cartoon skater,
A black night.

(Answer: Bart Simpson.)

Satnam Minhas & Michael Heslington (10)
Four Oaks Junior School

The Sound Of School

The buzz of the computer,
The ticking of the clock,
The squeaking of the chalk,
The locking of the lock.

The shouting of the teacher,
The writing of the pencil,
The screaming of the children,
The sketching of the stencil.

The flushing of the toilet,
The splashing of the sink,
The leaking of the pipes,
The gulping of the drink.

The watching of the watch,
The ringing of the bell,
I can't wait to get home,
Today has been hell!

Steven Micklewright (11)
Four Oaks Junior School

My Little Sister

My little sister is totally strange,
She picks her nose,
She wets the bed!

My little sister is really mad,
She stomps up the stairs,
She screams really loud.

My little sister is mega silly,
She runs round naked,
She cries like a baby!

Danny Knowles (10)
Four Oaks Junior School

Who Am I?

The king of Madrid,
A wife of pop,
Rushing sleek Ferrari,
Stepping up to the ball,
Getting ready to take his free-kick,
Ever-changing hairstyles.

Sponsored by everyone,
Expensive is his name,
Wore the famous number 7,
What else could he do for fame?

Not the quickest,
Not the slowest either,
One of the richest,
You can see why,
So who am I?

(Answer: David Beckham.)

Jack Etherton & Dexter Ealing (10)
Four Oaks Junior School

Who Am I?

The legend of legends
A servant of a lion
An endless forest
A light at the heart of Hell

Heart of the forest, hidden away
An enemy of a tyrant
A brother of a wolf
A silver arrow

The king of outlaws
A friend of a bear
A sign of freedom
A chink in the devil's armour.

(Answer: Robin Hood.)

Josh Wearing & Tom Silverton (11)
Four Oaks Junior School

Grannies Say Things Like . . .

Grannies say things like . . .
No television until you have finished your homework,
Eat with your mouth closed,
Turn that horrendous music down,
My goodness, haven't you grown,
No pudding until you have eaten those lovely vegetables,
Don't have any more sweets or you might be sick,
Mind you don't scratch the paintwork,
Take your shoes off before you go trampling over my
                                        nice cream carpet,
Be quiet, I'm talking,
Don't waste my phone bill on the Internet,
Sometimes grannies don't have a clue!

Mischa Howell (11)
Four Oaks Junior School

My Pet

My imaginary pet is as fat as a pig
And always digs,
When he finds something rare,
He never shares.

I love my pet dearly,
But does he know this. Really?
He wants to eat more and more,
Until his stomach goes sore.

My pet likes to play in the ice,
But he's not very nice,
He follows me around
And he doesn't make a sound.

Now he wants a friend,
To help the misery end,
When he goes to bed,
All his happy times are in his head!

Hoi Yan Wong (10)
Four Oaks Junior School

Snowy Day

It was a snowy day,
When I went out to play.
I built a big snowball
And threw it at my wall.

It was a snowy day,
I had a super day.
I went to the park
And my dog did a bark.

It was a snowy day
And I slept in some hay.
It was really cold,
So the hay turned to mould.

It was a snowy day
And the clouds turned to grey,
I played in the snow
And I did my best throw.

Jack Moore (10)
Four Oaks Junior School

The Weather

Rain dribbles down my nose,
The sun wakens the garden hose.
Thunder rumbles, lightning clashes,
Snow lands on my own eyelashes.

Hail smashes against the floor,
I watch as the rain starts to pour.
The wind starts to howl, trees sway to and fro,
Then ice creeps along and freezes the trowel.

The sun's heat is blistering,
Rain starts a splashing.
The snow glimmers from the sun,
Until I've had my fun!

Hannah Ward (10)
Four Oaks Junior School

Who Am I?

He is a musical instrument
A funny joke that makes people laugh
He is a prickly thorn
A stranger in the distance
He is a musical note
A rocky cliff
He is a tall dark figure
A bold boxing glove
He is a helping hand
A map to find directions
He is someone who solves problems
A person that people can go to to get cheered up
He is a loud whale's song
A red cross
Do you know who I am?
Can you guess?
Do you know?

Nadine Haskey (11)
Four Oaks Junior School

My Teacher Says

My teacher says, 'Get on!
Don't talk!
Stop copying!
I saw that!
That's not good enough!
Start again.
Go next door!
How many times have I spoken to you this week?
Go to the head teacher!
I can't wait till half-three!
Don't answer back!
I'll have to speak to your mum.
I will have to have a word with you!'
That's what my teacher says.

Oliver Swadkin (10)
Four Oaks Junior School

Kids Say Things Like This

Shut Up
Go away
You smell
I can't be bothered
Are we nearly there yet?
Mum
I want to watch 'Sister Sister'
I hate vegetables
I'm not eating *that*
I want a mobile phone
I don't feel very well
Can I have ten pounds?
I need the toilet
I've finished. Can you wipe my bottom?
I can't get these stupid tights on
Can I have a dog, a cat, a puppy and a kitten?
What's that smell?
What's that?
You're not coming to my birthday party
I'm not your friend
It's my go
That's what kids say.

Chelsea Binyon (10)
Four Oaks Junior School

Water

Where is it from?
What is it made of?
Why is it clear?
Why is it runny?
Why is it liquid?
Why does it freeze?
Why do we need it?
What is it for?

Stephanie Shoesmith (10)
Four Oaks Junior School

The Weather

I like the weather,
Especially the storm,
It rumbles and rumbles,
Until the weather turns warm.

I like the weather,
Especially the rain,
It pours and pours,
Until it drips off my windowpane.

I like the weather,
Especially the sun,
It shines and shines,
Until I've had my fun.

I like the weather,
Especially the lightning,
It flashes and flashes,
Until it's too frightening.

Kanar Talabani (11)
Four Oaks Junior School

The Sun And Moon

A blazing ball of fire,
A jewel up in the sky,
A burning shape above the Earth
Always floating by.

A white ball of decoration,
The destination of a space shuttle.
A park of floating items,
Always filling up.

Decorations of red and white
Decorating the sky,
But how did they form,
And I wonder why?

Stephen Davey (10)
Four Oaks Junior School

There's A Spot On My Nose

There's a spot on my nose
And it's bigger than my toes
With a big yellow top
Surely it will pop
I've squeezed it every day and night
Which just makes it glow all bright
There's a spot on my nose
And it's bigger than my toes
Then just last night
It started to itch and bite
So I shouted, *'Mum Mum Mum*
Come, come, come.'
So she ran to my cause
Without a pause
She pulled the tweezers out from her pocket
As quick as you pull a plug from a socket
She *squeezed* and *squeezed* and *squeezed*
And then the spot was finally seized.

Christina Loizou-Socratous (10)
Four Oaks Junior School

There's Gum In My Hair

Good grief! There's gum in my hair!
I rushed to the toilet and yanked my hair.
I moaned and screamed, 'It's not fair! It's not fair!'
My head was sore,
I didn't know what to do anymore.
Good grief! There's gum in my hair!
People found it hard not to stop and stare.
My hair has gone all sticky and icky,
Vicky and Nicky couldn't stop being meany,
So I pulled and I pulled with all my might,
And then it landed on Vicky's hair
With such a fright!
Now that serves her right!

Ruth Awunor (11)
Four Oaks Junior School

Names

Oh why can't I be called Alice,
Or maybe Ruth or Chelsea?
Shall it be Ella or Eleanor,
What about Katie or Kelsea?

I want to be called Lauren,
How about Kanar or Mischa?
Or maybe Steph or Hannah,
Or Laura or Trisa?

Oh why can't I change my name?
I hope my mum feels the same!

I know, Lydia,
Or maybe Grace or Christina?
Somthing like Becky or Nicole,
Maybe Charlotte or Tina?

Can't it be Nicola,
Or maybe Lucy or Denise?
It is possible to be Melissa or Alex,
Why not Emma or Venise?

Oh why can't I change my name?
I hope my mum feels the same!

Megan Brett (10)
Four Oaks Junior School

Love

Love means lots of things,
Like when boys and girls give rings.
Play nicely in that way!
That's what we all say.
Don't punch or hiss,
But do blow a kiss!
Love is what you should do,
Not just me . . .
But you too!

Sarah Kitteridge (8)
Four Oaks Junior School

Unanswered Questions

Why is your name star?
Why do you shine so bright?
Why are you so far away?
Why do you glint in the dark?

How do you move?
How do you breathe?
How did you get here?
How do you eat?

You are a source of light!
You are a saviour in the night!

What are you made from?
What do you do in your free time?
What do you survive on?
What is it that makes you twinkle?

Who founded you?
Who put you in the sky?
Who made you boiling hot?
Who is the one that made you glitter?

You are a source of light!
You are a saviour in the night!

Alice Brooks (10)
Four Oaks Junior School

Hope

Hope is a baby pink,
It smells like summer tulips
And tastes like melted marshmallows.
It sounds like water from a fountain
And it feels like a feather pillow.
Hope lives in the centre of a flower.

Lucy Palmer (9)
Four Oaks Junior School

Through That Door

(Based on 'Through That Door' by John Cotton)

Through that door
Is an ice island,
Where sea lions growl
And pirates murder,
Where under thin ice
Lies a great big chest
Full of pure gold
And pearls of silver.

Through that door
Is a tropical jungle,
Where snakes hiss
And beetles scuttle,
Where deep inside
Lies an old treasure box,
Surrounded by skulls
And hungry tigers.

Alex Maxwell-Keys (9)
Four Oaks Junior School

Snow

Snow, what is it?
Why did it fall?
Why is it called snow?
Why is it here?
Why is it cold?
Why is it white?
Why do we make snowmen?
Why do we have snowball fights?
Why does it melt?
Why?
Who knows?

Laura Davies-Hale (10)
Four Oaks Junior School

Through That Door

(Based on 'Through That Door' by John Cotton)

Through that door
Is a haunted castle,
Where ghosts howl
And Dracula lurks,
Where wolves prowl,
Teeth grind,
Doors bang,
Nothing's kind.

Through that door
Is a land of sweets,
Where candyfloss walks
And candy canes dance,
Where chocolate coins leap,
Haribo jump,
Penny chews play
And the fun never stops.

Harriette Watkins (10)
Four Oaks Junior School

Love

Love is blood red.
It smells like rose petals.
Love tastes like chocolate hearts with a strawberry centre,
It sounds like romantic voices.
Love feels warm and happy
And love lives in the person's heart you love.

Grace McDowall (10)
Four Oaks Junior School

Through That Door

(Based on 'Through That Door' by John Cotton)

Through that door
Is an underwater world,
Where mermaids dance
And dolphins splash,
Where down at the bottom
Fish play and
Whales sing and
Coral sways gently.

Through that door
Is a dream world,
Where magical castles sparkle
And dreams come true,
Where a magic fairy
From your dream
Comes to life
And looks after you.

Laura Cleveley (9)
Four Oaks Junior School

Old Age

Old age is like wrinkled skin,
It smells like a hospital ward
With something scary going on inside.
Old age tastes like gone-off milk
And sounds like a shrill whistle.
It feels like a headache that won't go away.
Old age lives at the bottom of the world.

Ellie Goodman (9)
Four Oaks Junior School

Through That Door

(Based on 'Through That Door' by John Cotton)

Through that door
Is an underwater world,
Where whales float
And mermaids glide,
Where young fish hide
Behind chests of gold,
And pearls lie,
Never to be seen.

Through that door
Lies a land of dreams,
Where clouds float
And stars shimmer,
Where children sleep
With no cares,
And their favourite things
Stay forever.

Through that door
Is an icy land,
Where polar bears
And penguins play,
Where walruses slide
To catch their tea,
And fling the bones
Where they please.

Sam Neal (10)
Four Oaks Junior School

Through That Door

(Based on 'Through That Door' by John Cotton)

Through that door
Is an underwater world
Where coral sways
And fish swim,
Where turtles lie
On golden sand,
Where dolphins play
In the sparkling sun.

Through that door
Is a rainforest,
Where trees are blue
And monkeys red,
Where fruit changes colour,
And birds too,
The sun shines green
Through the jungle.

Through that door
Is a land of sweets,
Where Haribo fight
And chocolate never melts,
Where people are jelly babies
And houses are lollipop sticks,
With arches of candy canes
And roads of gum.

Melissa Chiam (9)
Four Oaks Junior School

Kids Say Things Like . . .

Go away,
Shut up,
Boring,
I hate you,
Do I have to?
Are we there yet?
I need the toilet.
What does that mean?
I'm telling of you.
I don't want to go to school.
I'm not eating that.
Whatever.
I'm going to my room.
I don't want to go to bed.
I'm hungry.
I want that one,
Please Mum,
Mum!

Amie Haigh (11)
Four Oaks Junior School

Hope

Hope is happy flowers!
Hope smells like fresh grass.
Hope tastes like melting chocolate.
Hope sounds like a flying breeze.
Hope feels smooth and silky.
Hope lives in the air,
Its colour is light green.

Haleigh Mathews (10)
Four Oaks Junior School

Kids Say Things Like . . .

Go away!
Shut up!
I hate you
Give it!
You're stupid!
You smell!
I want seconds!
Down with homework!
Are we there yet?
I wanna go home!
I can't be bothered!
I'm hungry!
I need the toilet!
Oh, come on!
Hurry up!
I'm bored!
Give me a go!
Do I have to?
I didn't do it!
Come on!
I'm telling!
Change the channel!
What?
That is what kids say.

Joe Wright (10)
Four Oaks Junior School

Hope

Hope is sky-blue.
It smells like a spring morning.
Hope tastes like strawberry ice cream.
It sounds like a golden harp,
It feels like velvet.
Hope lives in an angel's heart.

Jacob Beechey (10)
Four Oaks Junior School

Children Say Things

Children say things like . . .
I'm not your friend,
I hate you,
I'm hungry,
Are we there yet?
I don't want to.
Cool.
What?
I don't want to go to school.
I'm bored.
Shut up!
I need the toilet.
Ha! Ha!
Go away.
I don't care.
I don't want to go to bed.
That's horrible.
Change the channel,
I'm scared.
I want that.
I don't have to.
Give me some money.
Finished.

Luke Winkless (10)
Four Oaks Junior School

Hope

Hope is yellow,
It smells just like lavender.
Hope tastes like honey,
It sounds like birds singing.
Hope feels like when you run your fingers down silk,
It lives in a field of flowers.

Robyn Coles (10)
Four Oaks Junior School

Through That Door

(Based on 'Through That Door' by John Cotton)

Through that door
Lies an aqua land,
Where dolphins swim
And seaweed sways,
Where sand gleams
On the ocean floor,
With treasure buried
Long before.

Through that door
Lies an Arctic waste,
Where penguins dive
And sea lions swim,
Where polar bears wander,
Ice glaciers gleam
And wrecks of ships
Forever rest.

Through that door
Lies a tropical jungle
Where monkeys screech
And preen themselves,
Where a million insects
Gather and creep,
And layers of trees
Shelter and keep.

Richard Shotton (10)
Four Oaks Junior School

Old Age

Old age is brown,
It smells like wilting flowers.
Old age tastes steamy,
It sounds like whispers.
It feels bumpy and wrinkly.
Old age lives in a retirement home.

James Quance (9)
Four Oaks Junior School

Anger And Pain

Anger

Anger is red,
It smells like smoke.
Anger tastes of burnt food,
It sounds like iron against metal.
It feels of sharp points.
Anger lives in the heart of a volcano.

Pain

Pain is black,
It smells like blood.
Pain tastes of salt.
It sounds like two swords clashing,
It feels like the point of a spike.
Pain lives in the middle of a war.

Jordan Arnett (9)
Four Oaks Junior School

Hope

Hope is pure white, like silk cloth.
It smells like fairy cakes cooking.
Hope tastes sweet, like strawberry meringue!
It sounds like birds singing and chanting.
Hope feels like lying on a sun bed with extreme relaxation.
Hope lives in the bottom of your heart,
Curing you from all evil.

Jack Whiting (9)
Four Oaks Junior School

Through My Binoculars

I can see a long-armed monkey,
High upon a brown oak tree.
It's far too cute,
I'm too scared to shoot,
It's like a squirrel going nutty.

Now I see a slithering snake,
I think it's a nest it wants to make.
Its mouth is so wide,
I will stay on this side,
Phew, now it's taking a break.

Oh, look over there,
It's a huge grizzly bear.
Quick get the gun,
I'm sure it must weigh a ton,
Or maybe we should throw the chair!

Matthew Litwinowicz (9)
Four Oaks Junior School

Kitty

There's a little kitty sitting on a mat,
Here comes a little brown sneaky rat.
She went to pounce
And it looked like a bounce,
She was just being an ordinary cat.

The little kitty went back to her mat,
Then came flying in a big, black bat.
She went to pounce
And it looked like a bounce,
She was just being an ordinary cat.

Katie Etherton (8)
Four Oaks Junior School

Fear

I'm 1,000 years old
And I'm as *scary* as Frankenstein,
Or anything scary really.
I've got *frightening* brothers,
Freddie and Scram.
One's like a scarecrow and the other's like a grim reaper.
I'll tell you a secret,
I'm afraid of sunlight and
Even sometimes, afraid of myself.
I've set my record of scaring 400 people,
More than my brothers could do.
By the way, if you want to know my real name,
It is *Count Dracula,*
And I'm going to suck your blood.

Charlotte Montgomery (10)
Great Bridge Primary School

Fear

I am as scary as a vampire.
I'm a hundred and eleven years old.
I live in a place called Elm Street.
If you dare go down there, you will be meat.
My sister is called Simara,
Her hair is black as a sack.
My brother is Freddy, whose fingernails
Are as sharp as shark's teeth.
I would love to scare you one of these days,
So don't come near me.
I'm not telling you what I'm scared of,
So leave!
Or I will make you turn into one of me.
Dirty, damp, fierce and to scare,
And I will take you to my lair.

Tyler Durnall (11)
Great Bridge Primary School

Sea, Through The Senses

Look at the sea,
Clear, aquamarine and shimmering,
Raging like a bull at a red flag.

Listen to the sea,
Raging, shimmering and aquamarine,
Clear as a crystal in the sun.

Touch the sea,
Aquamarine, clear and raging,
Shimmering like some great lip gloss.

Taste the sea,
Shimmering, raging and clear,
As aquamarine jewels in a cabinet.

Smell the sea,
Clear, shimmering and aquamarine,
Raging like a lion after its dinner.

Jade Wyatt (10)
Great Bridge Primary School

My Dog

My dog is a golden Labrador,
He has big brown eyes like chocolate.
His name is Mitch.
He is fat and cuddly like a teddy bear,
That is my dog!

My dog loves to crunch on bones,
He also loves to play fight with my dad.
He is always nudging you for fuss.
I think he is just lovely.
He is always wagging his tail,
That is my *dog!*

Samantha Bates (10)
Great Bridge Primary School

A To Z

A is for an alligator asking for food,
B is for baboon bouncing around and eating bananas,
C is for a cat coughing,
D is for a dog dancing around,
E is for an elephant eating eggs,
F is for a frog jumping around,
G is for a goat charging at me.
H is for a horse eating some hay,
I is for an iguana eating flies,
J is for a jaguar jumping past the cheetah,
K is for a koala bear drinking cola,
L is for a lion licking lollies,
M is for a monkey eating crisps,
N is for a gnat biting at you all night,
O is for an octopus eating fish,
P is for a penguin diving in the sea,
Q is for a quail quacking noisily,
R is for a rabbit nibbling a carrot,
S is for a snake slithering and slimy,
T is for a tiger eating meat,
U is for ugly like an orang-utan,
V is for a vole living by the water,
W is for a wolf, scary at night,
X is for an X-ray fish swimming in the sea,
Y is for a yak, a bit like a moose,
Z is for a zebra looking at his wife.

Charlotte Wyatt (9)
Great Bridge Primary School

Seasons

S pring is full of beautiful lilac flowers
P ink flowers all over our lovely garden
R unning and jumping in the garden all day long
I n the garden my mum and dad relax in the sun
N ibbling on crisps all day
G rating cheese for our sandwiches.

S ummer is always hot, the sun never goes away
U mbrellas are not needed at all
M ice squeaking, looking for cheese
M ums and dads relaxing in the summer sun
E very day we jump and play
R ain never comes in summer.

A tree has got absolutely no leaves left on its branches
U mbrellas are needed just for when it's raining
T ightly tucked up in bed
U nderneath the soil in the garden, worms wriggling around.
M ice eating their cheese
N ice warm drinks of a night.

W inter is horrible and cold
I cy nights every night
N athan, my brother, plays with me inside
T onight we will wrap up in bed cosily
E very night it's cold outside
R ain always comes out.

Zoë Allen (9)
Great Bridge Primary School

Don't Do

Don't do,
Don't do,
Don't throw your toys at your dad,
Don't shove your toes up your sister's nose,
Don't wash yourself in the mud,
Don't draw over your brother's homework,
Don't have flies for dinner,
What do you think I am?
Some kind of fool?

Don't do,
Don't do,
Don't flick rubbers at your dad,
Don't throw your sister's homework out of the window,
Don't eat worms for dinner,
Don't make pie with snails and ketchup,
What do you think I am?
Some kind of fool?

Charlotte Cox (9)
Great Bridge Primary School

West Brom

W onderful West Brom will beat you all
E veryone's scared of the baggie boy
S uperb players, better than the rest
T hey'll finish top, no matter what.

B rilliant, beautiful, classical team
R ubbish Cockney Gunners, you're all a load of cheaters
O verall the greatest team in Division One
M an U get lost, we've beaten you 2-0.

West Brom!

Daniel Leatherland (10)
Great Bridge Primary School

Who Am I?

Once upon a time
I heard a rhyme,
I'm going to tell you
Because it starts with a moo.

Moo I say
At the end of the day,
I eat grass,
I also play brass.

I live on a dirty farm,
No animals ever bring me harm,
I also live with a big, fat pig
Who wears a yellow wig.

It's the end of a long, hot day
But there's one more question!
Who am I?

(Answer: A cow).

Katie Williams (10)
Great Bridge Primary School

My Gran

I love my gran,
She's the best,
But sometimes she can be a pest.

She lets me use her telephone,
And I can play the xylophone.

When she's alone, she likes me there,
So she can cuddle my teddy bear.

I love my gran,
She's the best.
She's better than the rest.

Megan Wildman (9)
Great Bridge Primary School

Football

F ootball is a very good sport, although you might get hurt
O f course you might think the boots look funny, but they feel
like shoes
O uch, he has just done a two-footed tackle, that's got to hurt
T here is one goalkeeper and eleven football players on each team
B ut when you head the ball, the ball hurts your head
A lthough the goalkeeper looks bored, he has got the best position
L ook at that, he has just headed the ball, I bet he has got
a headache
L ook at that, he has just scored his third goal, he has got
his hat-trick.

Kevin Clayton (10)
Great Bridge Primary School

Summer Is Fun

S ummer is fun, I like to run
U ntil winter comes I can play every day
M ums are talking while we shout
M aybe I'll call out for my mates
E ating ice cream with my friends
R unning to the park with the hot air going past my face

I nto the cool shade I go
S omething tells me I'll be here all day

F irst I play in the cool fun park
U can play for ages and ages
N early time to go, but I can't wait for next year to come.

Sundeep Kaur (10)
Great Bridge Primary School

Geoff Horsfield

H orsfield should play for England
O h yes he should, you know
R ight on, he's number one
S cored against Wolves, he's a
F antastic man
I ncredible Horsfield when he gets the ball
E ngland's supporting hero
L anding with a goal
D anny, that's me, Horsfield's number one fan.

Daniel Bell (11)
Great Bridge Primary School

Mr Jabberwoo

Mr Jabberwoo is as thin as a ruler,
Tall as a giraffe
And has a bit of a tummy too.
He can be rude and cruel.
He has a long, pointed nose,
His red hair rests on his yellow head,
Which is shaped like an egg.
He has blue eyes and brown teeth.
That's Mr Jabberwoo.

Laura Summers (10)
Great Bridge Primary School

Leaves

L ong leaves, short leaves,
E very single tree losing lots of leaves all the time.
A lways invited to the grass's home for a cup of tea,
V ery intelligent, old and crinkly leaves.
E legant and independent leaves,
S ome are very snooty, so beware, leave the leaves alone.

Daniel Weaver (10)
Great Bridge Primary School

Birthday Time

B irthday times are the best
I always get invited
R ight on time every party
T ime is ticking on very, very quickly
H i Rachel, that's my friend
D ad said he would be back
A t 5pm tonight
Y eah, I'm having a great time.

T reats like sweets and a lucky bag
I love all of those things
M y best friend's party is over
E very time is the best.

Paige Byrne (9)
Great Bridge Primary School

If I Could Be Famous

If I could be famous,
I would give money to the poor
And build them a new house.

If I could be famous,
I would have people come into my house
And we would have a party.

If I could be famous,
I would let kids backstage
And we would sing and dance together.

If I could be famous,
I would travel around the world
And take poor children with me.

Hollie Willett (9)
Great Bridge Primary School

Fear

As old as a rusty engine,
I am 159 years old.
I am as spooky as a ghost ship.
I was born on a ghost ship.
My brother and sister are as horrible as tornados.
I have a brother named Dracula and a sister named Anger.
I have clothes, angry like lions.
My favourite types of clothes are fire shirts,
Dragon shirts and robes like vampires.
I have a forbidding home,
I live in a haunted house.
My greatest ambition is to get rid of happiness
And bring fear to the universe.
My greatest fears are determination,
Courageous people and happiness.
My greatest success was forcefully feeding
Fearful fools with *fear!*
Cross me if you dare!

Devinder Sangoo (11)
Great Bridge Primary School

Beware Of Fear

Beware the danger of Rabla Gooster!
Born in an abandoned chicken farm,
He can cause you serious harm.
Beware the fiery flames of his sister, Inferno,
Born in a heated blow-bursting volcano.
Both as evil as the Devil,
But beware even more of me - Fear.
Don't come near!
I will put a curse on you.
I live in a raggedy cave with lava.
Beware of fear.

Ritesh Patel (10)
Great Bridge Primary School

Sweeties

Sweeties, sweeties,
They're so tasty,
My belly is full.
My mum and dad keep
Taking them off me,
And keep getting me to eat vegetables,
But I always get away from the table.
I run from home to my mate's house
With lots of sweeties.
Sweeties.

Kyle Guest (10)
Great Bridge Primary School

Fear

Who am I?
Guess my age?
Bubbling, blasting badly
From my cold, black heart of stone.
I'm evil - the Devil is my brother.
We live in a deep, dark, daunting back alley.
I despise happiness.
If you see me, you're in for a scare my friend!

Christopher James (11)
Great Bridge Primary School

England

E ngland, England, they beat the rest
N obody can beat them, they're the best
G ermany lost 5-1, and me and
L iam cheered England on
A nd we lost to Brazil
N o England were not brill, so
D on't mess with the best. *England!*

Liam Rickards (9)
Great Bridge Primary School

Autumn Leaves

Autumn leaves are thin and crisp
As they swirl around and around in the autumn breeze.

Autumn leaves are crunchy and crumpled
When you stomp through them.

Autumn leaves crunch in your warm hands and fingers,
Then they squash and flutter down to the ground in tiny pieces.

Autumn leaves have feelings, I believe!

Georgina Richards (11)
Great Bridge Primary School

Happiness

Happiness is my name
And smiling is my game.
All I do all day
Is fill people in my way.

I like to be me,
Nice, easy and free.
Everyone loves me
And that's just the way to be.

Kirsty Hipkins (11)
Great Bridge Primary School

Leaf Poem

The leaves glide to the ground,
Flowing round, round, round.
As they bend and twist,
Their colours shine in the sun.
When you walk through a bunch of leaves
You can hear the crunching and crackling.
The bright autumn colours,
Red, yellow, light brown, etc.

Paige Moore (10)
Great Bridge Primary School

My Senses Of The Sea

Look at the sea, turquoise and calm,
Shimmering under the red-hot sun,
At times as fierce as a great white shark.

Listen to the sea, peaceful and calm,
Shimmering is the sea as I hear fierce tides and waves
Shooting up high, bluey-turquoise like marine fish.

Touch the sea as I feel the water hardly calm at all,
Shimmering turquoise as I rush it through my fingers.

Taste the sea as I see it so turquoise,
When I feel it running down my throat,
It becomes fierce, then so calm,
I then stare at the beautiful shimmering sea.

Smell the sea, the salty essence as I inhale it,
The shimmering sea fierce, also calm as a sleeping cat.

Sharondeep Shergill (10)
Great Bridge Primary School

Leaves

The autumn breeze in the night,
The browny-orange leaves gliding in the air,
All the leaves talking to each other with their crackling voices.
The sound of the leaves making a crunching noise
And a little whisper in the air.
All the leaves on the floor as if they're dead,
And the golden colours shining in the sky.
All the leaves fluttering around us as if they're young, lively children.
With the moon going down and the sun coming up,
The leaves just wait until late in the night.

Lucie Bonehill (11)
Great Bridge Primary School

Caterpillars

C aterpillars crawling across the concrete floor
A nts scuttling for food, trying to miss people's feet
T igers roaring in the sizzling sun
E els swimming in the calm, deep blue sea
R abbits rushing around on the green, crunchy grass
P enguins flopping side to side
I nsects flying like my brother's electronic aeroplane
L ions roaring in the Australian desert
L ovely butterflies fluttering in the sky
A pes swinging from branch to branch
R hinos rushing around like your mum when she is late for work
S orry, all those creatures I have missed out, but this is
    where the poem ends, for I have done an acrostic poem and I
    have described all the creatures I can.

Jasmeena Samrai (10)
Great Bridge Primary School

Football

I like the buzzing chatter of children
And how I loved to be played with.
I don't like to be put in the classroom corner for hours,
Because I want to get out and have some exercise.
I'm afraid of rusty nails piercing my flesh and causing me infections,
I lose all my breath and I can never have it back.
I'm happy when I hit the net, the crowd goes wild,
And people run with their hands in the air, cheering.
I'm sad when I see my friends being infected by that dreaded
                                        rusty nail.
My friends lose their breath and they are unable to get it back.
I'd rather be invincible, so I can never be
Hurt and breathless ever again.

Stacey Guest (11)
Great Bridge Primary School

Autumn Leaves

Leaves, leaves, everywhere, leaves all kinds of shapes,
Star, round, oval and many more,
Twisting and flying through the breezy air,
Like a hot air balloon, fluttering ant twirling,
Higher and higher until it stops still,
It can't fly any further, it starts to let its
Tenderness float to the juicy green ground.
Its sandy yellow body starts to crinkle
And whistle through the deep blue sky.
As it flies down, it flutters over the shadowy trees
Until it stops flat on the grassy area, tender and still.
It can't be bothered to fly any further on another autumn day.
His brothers and sisters will follow him.
Leaves, leaves, everywhere leaves.

Halima Atika Hussain (11)
Great Bridge Primary School

Trapped In A Town

The smoke was increasing,
Clean air was decreasing,
The clouds were so grey,
It was another terrible day.

The skies were all black,
Workers had no time to slack,
The pollution was rising,
As the fishes were dying.

The factories were so prison-like,
But still workers worked all day and night.
The time went on and on so slow,
But workers had no place to go.

Jordanne Doody (11)
Great Bridge Primary School

Survivor

The tide gathers on the seashore,
The sand is eaten and gone,
Ivory gulls soar overhead
Singing the ocean song.

Beneath the waves the gilled ones scatter,
Hiding in crevices and weed.
The great blue whale arises,
A glorious sight to see, indeed.

The almighty mammal towers over in silent might,
Eyes that hold no thought of hate or sorrow,
Look upon the shore in muted wisdom,
Then she is gone, the tide is all to be heard.

Sylvia Dias (11)
Great Bridge Primary School

The Stylish Cat

Behold the cat, snowy-white,
A pair of trainers on her feet,
Jogging along to her music beat.

Does her baseball top look too big?
Does her cap look too bright?
Do her sunglasses look too dark?

Does it matter? There she goes
Jogging in her stylish clothes,
Listening to her music beat.

Daniel Norton (10)
Great Bridge Primary School

Smoketown - Days Gone By

Tired and weak workers, work their life away
As the loud screaming machines deafen the city.
The workers sigh and moan in distress,
As they work day and night and no one has pity.

They work and watch the smoke blow high,
Polluting the land around.
The air they breathe is filthy and black
As it twirls and swirls down to the ground.

Everyone starts to choke,
As up goes the smoke,
But that's how it is in Smoketown.

Amie-Lea Sambrook (10)
Great Bridge Primary School

Me - Fear!

As old as can be,
I'm made to frighten who I can see.
I was born to be evil,
So I awoke from the dead,
The blood that is red
I drink in bed.
I live on Elm Street
And I have feet which
Smell like meat.
I'm here to scare,
If you care, you won't dare,
So beware!

Arfana Hussain (11)
Great Bridge Primary School

If I Could . . .

If I could be famous,
I would put money in the bank
And save it up.
If I could swim like a dolphin
I would jump through a hoop
And catch a fish.
If I could be fast
I'd run as fast as I could
And get to school on time.
If I could be wrong
I might take wrong turns
And make mistakes.
If I could be more clever
I'd tell people when they got things wrong
And help people.
If I could be very strong
I'd do weight training,
Pick up heavy people.
If I could be a teacher,
I would teach children
And tell them what to do.
If I could have wings,
I would fly in the sky
And go around the world.

Ajay Singh (10)
Great Bridge Primary School

Autumn

Autumn leaves are crunchy and crisp,
They fly around in the peaceful autumn breeze.
Autumn leaves crumple when you walk through.
When you hold them in your hand they break into pieces.
I believe they have feelings.
They flow so gently with their beautiful colours,
And then they fall so peaceful to the ground.

Rachel Bennett (10)
Great Bridge Primary School

The Haunted House

'Who is there? Show yourself!' I shouted,
As a tiny orb zoomed out the kitchen door.
An eerie silence filled the air,
Clarissa clenched my arm tightly!
The silence was broken by the loud slam on the floor.

A light, spooky wail filled the air
As a figure scratched at the door.
Phil went up the creaky stairs . . .
I went in the kitchen, Clarissa went to the front room.
Taps came on, alarms went off
And a small plant lifted on its own.

The gate slammed, plants flew
And ornaments smashed,
Lights switched on and off,
Spooky sounds at normally silent places.

'We should go,' we agreed.
The sounds faded and things stopped moving
And all was normal as we left.

Dale Peach (9)
Hatherton Lane Primary School

My Football Team

I play for a team called Beechdale
We are third in the league.
We run on the field, up and down
Stretching our legs, getting fitter.
We always have training
Even if it's raining.
We are going to be the best in Division Two
And when we're finished we'll say, 'Phew!'

Sean Pinnington (9)
Hatherton Lane Primary School

The Haunted House

'Who's there, is there anybody here?' I whispered.
There were noises coming towards me.
'Is there anybody there? Answer me,' I loudly spoke.
'Open the door.'
Creaks were coming towards me from the house.
There were flickering lights,
I started to get scared,
I was nervous.
'Answer me, open the door, I'll wait.'
I shouted loudly.
I heard more footsteps coming towards me.
There were noises coming from the house.
I quietly announced,
'Who's there? I know somebody's there,
I can hear you moving.
Answer me.'

Demi-Lee Ranford (9)
Hatherton Lane Primary School

The Listeners

'Did you hear that?' I whispered,
It looks like an eerie, haunted house.

The wind is howling through the branches of the trees,
I can see a shadow,
Scratching on the wooden door.
There is a person trapped,
He is waiting to get out,
I am scared and shivering,
The trees rustled in the wind.
Something is coming this way,
There is a crackle underfoot.
'Did you hear that?'

Stefen Dukes (9)
Hatherton Lane Primary School

The Teachers' School

There was a school
That was so cool
There were lots of children
That played the fool.
They swam in the pool,
That was cool.

There was a teacher
That had a heater
She had a fight with Mrs Wright
And beat her.

There was a classroom
That had a bathroom
Where all the children used to zoom.

There was a dinner cook
That always read her book
And she used to give a crafty look.

Keelli Davis (10)
Hatherton Lane Primary School

My Brother

I have a brother, his name is Dave
Please do not come by him or you'll be afraid.
In the moonlight he will give you a fright,
He turns into a wolf when the moon is bright!

When he's a wolf watch for his bite,
When he's not, he won't hurt you.
I like him best when he's a boy,
When he's a wolf he will annoy.

Chloe O'Brien (9)
Hatherton Lane Primary School

Animals

Crocodile, crocodile,
With sharp teeth.
Crocodile, crocodile,
Is a food thief.
Crocodile, crocodile,
Moves like a sniper.
Crocodile, crocodile,
With speed like a viper.

Tiger, tiger,
Is black and gold.
Tiger, tiger,
You'll never feel the cold.
Tiger, tiger,
Hunts all day.
Tiger, tiger,
He'll catch your prey.

Parrot, parrot,
Colours so bright.
Parrot, parrot,
Such a wonderful sight.
Parrot, parrot,
Sits in the tree.
Parrot, parrot
Is always flying free.

Jonathon Duckett (10)
Hatherton Lane Primary School

Animals

Animals are weird and bright,
Animals are slow at night.
Animals are grizzly and rizzly,
Animals are fat and sizzly.
Animals are sharp and scary,
Animals are small and hairy.

Daniel Fellows (9)
Hatherton Lane Primary School

The Ghost

The ghost got up
And had some toast,
Then he wanted a Sunday roast.

The ghost sat in a wheelchair,
Then he decided to have a pear.
When he ate the pear,
He had to go into intensive care!

The ghost went outside,
Then he wanted to go on the slide,
So he got in a car and went for a ride.

He went off down a country lane,
Rattling his rusty chains,
Then suddenly he had a pain
And they never saw the ghost again.

Leanne Wootton (10)
Hatherton Lane Primary School

Magnificent Aeroplanes

An aeroplane flies up and down
And it flies round and round,
Aeroplanes are very loud,
If you drive one you will be proud.
They will stand,
When they land.

Aeroplanes zoom in the sky,
People see them passing by,
How I wish I could go,
Above the clouds which are not low.

Ashley Harvey (10)
Hatherton Lane Primary School

The Lone Tramp

It was dark, gloomy and frightening
In the forest there was lightning
There was a lonely tramp walking along
He saw something that looked like King Kong.

But he has a lonely life in front of him
But he must fear it now
Goodbye Mr Tramp
Goodbye Mr Tramp
Is life a trap?
Here have some food.

Now you are rich and that's good
Welcome to the wealthy life
Mr Wealthy
Mr Wealthy
Some people care about you.

Thomas Corrigan (10)
Hatherton Lane Primary School

The Listener

Did you remember I was coming?
Because I am back again.
The wind was blowing the trees,
Whoosh, whoosh.
The trees were swaying from side to side,
Pitter-patter, pitter-patter.
Raindrops tapping,
Splashing on the window sill.
A full moon right overhead,
Stars all around.
Silently bats glide past the window,
Is that a noise I hear?

Amber-Jade Bennett (10)
Hatherton Lane Primary School

Fairground

Enormous mammoth swirling loudly
above the trees on the track.
Enormous mammoth twizzling slowly
on the track that hurt my back.
Enormous mammoth moving fast
on the track that gave me a heart attack.
Enormous mammoth speeding quickly
down a ramp that made my back crack.

Running lion running carefully around the trees
then it found some peas.
Running lion rushing brightly to have a walk
but then it stalked.
Running lion walking quietly past some trees
and made me sneeze.

Blinding mist running anxiously above the trees
then hurting my knees.
Blinding mist walking carefully around a wall
that made me fall.
Blinding mist rushing noisily in a park
and then it went dark.

Mathew Rollinson (8)
Hatherton Lane Primary School

The Haunted House

The rain is rattling
The gates are clattering
The wind is rushing
The gargoyle is crushing
The house is creepy
The graveyard is freaky
The thunder is booming
The lightning is striking.

Thomas Wain (10)
Hatherton Lane Primary School

Isabel

Isabel met a boy called Arron
Isabel said you look like Karen
Isabel said, 'Come to the beach
then I'll buy you a little peach.'
Isabel said, 'It's 10 o'clock
we must get home.'
Then Arron started to moan
Isabel, Isabel, Isabel.

Isabel met an enormous bear
Isabel said, 'I love your fur.'
Isabel said, 'Pleased to meet you.'
The bear said, 'Don't worry,
I won't eat you.'
Isabel said, 'You silly bear
Don't be my friend, I don't care!'

Joanna Waddison (9)
Hatherton Lane Primary School

My Best Friend

My friend is the best friend anybody could ever have.
His arms and legs are quite big,
His hair is blond,
His clothes are neat every day
And every single morning he wears his watch,
He's clean all day
And teeth are brushed.
He's got an eight geared bike,
He's got very good CDs
And he's my best friend,
Called Ashley Harvey.

Matthew Jones (9)
Hatherton Lane Primary School

The Rhyming School

There was a school,
   Near a pool,
      There was a boy who was cool.

There was a teacher,
   That had a heater,
      Every day her room was neater.

There was a bully,
   He lived down a gully,
      He ate a lot of curry.

The school was tall,
   They held their ball,
      In the grand hall.

Laura Fisher (9)
Hatherton Lane Primary School

Isabel

Isabel met a boy called Dale,
The boy said, 'It's a big gale.'
Isabel said, 'But you've got long nails
And you have a lot of mail.'

Isabel met a cat,
Isabel said, 'I like your hat
And I like your mat.'
And so they went by the fire and sat.

Isabel saw a bird fly,
It made her want to cry
And it was very shy
And then it flew back into the sky.

Laura Missen (10)
Hatherton Lane Primary School

Tiger Began

He took the stripes off a zebra crossing
He took the smoothness of leather
And made his coat.

For his teeth
He took the sharpness of a knife
He took the blade of a razor
He took the shyness of a mirror.

From the airport
He took the speed of a plane
He took the quietness of a mouse
For his movement.

Then from the animals
He took the growl of a dog
He took the slyness of a fox
To make his voice

And tiger was born.

Luke Talbot (10)
Hatherton Lane Primary School

The Tiger

The tiger leaps
The tiger eats
The tiger roars
He has big paws.
The tiger sees some big, chunky bees
He loves lots of peas
And he found some shiny keys.

Amy Henworth (9)
Hatherton Lane Primary School

The Lady Of Shalott

(Based on 'The Lady Of Shalott' by Alfred Lord Tennyson)

She looked down on the happy sight,
The people were merry and bright.
She turned to see the knights fight.
She went to the window to see the sunlight.
    Too many towered Camelot.

She saw a handsome man riding by
She looked through the mirror, she was shy.
She was miserable and gave a sigh,
    The lady of Shalott.

She ran down from the tower,
It had already been one hour.
She grabbed a pink flower.
The mirror cracked from the curse's power,
    From many towered Camelot.

She went outside and began to cry
She went to the boat to lie.
She shouted, 'Please let me die.'
    The lady of Shalott.

She got her coat around her
As lightning struck the fur.
She said, 'Please let me die, Sir.'
How sad nobody cared for her,
    From many towered Camelot.

She gave a shake
And fell in the lake.
Her blood froze,
She fell in repose,
    The lady of Shalott.

Lucy Hunt (9)
Hatherton Lane Primary School

The Lady Of Shalott

(Based on 'The Lady Of Shalott' by Alfred Lord Tennyson)

There lived a lady in a castle,
Her name was the lady of Shalott.
She was a beautiful lady,
Her castle was called Camelot.

The castle was big,
With four grey walls and four towers,
Her casement windows looked down.

The river flowed down and down,
Barley and rye grew in the fields.
The village people didn't know who she was,
Or what she looked like.

The lady of Shalott had a curse upon her,
She couldn't ever leave the castle.
The mirror was there,
She couldn't look down through the window.

There was a knight called Sir Lancelot.
When the lady of Shalott heard him,
She looked out of the window.

The mirror cracked from side to side,
It went dark.
The lady of Shalott left the castle,
Found a boat,
She wrote her name on the prow.
She died as her blood froze.
Sire Lancelot said a prayer for
The lady of Shalott.

Melissa Parsons (9)
Hatherton Lane Primary School

Fairground

Roller coaster zooming tightly above the water,
Roller coaster twisting fast with mother and daughter.

Roller coaster spinning slowly on the track,
Roller coaster twirling excitedly with a big crack.

Big wheel turning softly in the air,
Big wheel flying smoothly, messing up my hair.

Haunted castle clicking loudly on the track,
Haunted castle swishing slowly, I hope it doesn't have a crack.

Haunted castle creaking eerily in the room,
Haunted castle cracking quietly, I don't like it if I'm doomed.

Cyclops twirling speedily in the air,
Cyclops turning smoothly, untidying my hair.

Cyclops whirling softly in the breeze,
Cyclops spinning swiftly, it gives me a freeze.

Haley Bagnall (9)
Hatherton Lane Primary School

Colonel Fazackerley And This Ghost

(Based on 'Colonel Fazackerley' by Charles Causley)

Colonel Fazackerley Butterworth-Toast
He didn't know what to do with his ghost.
The ghost scared him and his friend Tim
The ghost scared everyone and then the ghost had gone.

Colonel Fazackerley Butterworth-Toast
Was having a problem with a difficult ghost.
The ghost came back and he tried to attack,
When he saw the people he fell onto a steeple
And nobody saw the ghost again.

Nicholas Edwards (10)
Hatherton Lane Primary School

Winter, Winter

Winter dazzling
In the frozen park
The crunchy leaves fell to the floor
The frosty wind swayed,
Swirled round and round
And then moved on.

Winter sparkled
On the icy roads
By the gleaming sea.
Jack Frost laid a sheet of snow
On the floor
And then moved on.

Winter crept
From the sky,
Twirling and turning
Round and round
Dancing and prancing
And then moved on.

Winter darted
Leaving snow through the dark woods
Icicles spreading the coldness.

Rebekah Harvey (10)
Hatherton Lane Primary School

Bonfire Booms

A dark night
   A bright night
      Best of all
         It's Bonfire Night.

Ashley Silvester (10)
Hatherton Lane Primary School

Cheetah Began

Cheetah began
He took the speed of a plane
He took the claws of an eagle
And made his feet.

For his head
He took the brains of a fox
He took stars for his eyes
He took the sharpness of a dagger
For his teeth.

From the duvet
He took the softness of a feather
He took the colour of gold for his body
With the blackness of the night for his spots
For his body.

Then for a tail
He took the shape of a brush
He took the bristles of a mat
To make his tail

And cheetah was made.

Bradley Sanders (11)
Hatherton Lane Primary School

Water

Water, water on the floor
Water, water more and more

Water, water in the drain
Water, water always rain

Water, water in the taps
Water, water drips off caps.

Ryan Lycett (10)
Hatherton Lane Primary School

Fairground

Massive roller coaster zooming around the trees,
Massive roller coaster twirling fast in the breeze.
Massive roller coaster twisting scarily round and round,
Massive roller coaster squashing noisily, dips into the ground.

Ice cream melting slowly in the sun,
Ice cream dripping silently, what fun.
Ice cream cooling nicely in the heat,
Ice cream standing quietly in by my feet.

Swimming pool shining nicely in the sun,
Swimming pool lying lovely with my mum.
Swimming pool swiftly, smoothly what fun,
Swimming pool standing smoothly, cooling in the sun.

Lauren Stanton (8)
Hatherton Lane Primary School

The School

Children eating nicely at the table
Children drinking slowly by a cable
Children collecting fast by a table
Children sitting comfortably by Mabel.

Teachers shouting loudly in the grass
Teachers teaching quietly in the class
Teachers sneezing fast outside
Teachers listening slowly outlined.

Kids running fast on the grass
Kids jumping slowly for the pass.
Kids staring sharply in the air
Kids standing excited in the fair.

Damon Harvey (8)
Hatherton Lane Primary School

Snake Began

He took the silver from the moon,
He took the green of the grass
And made his coat.

For his voice
He took the hissing like the screech of a mouse,
He took the rumble of a volcano,
He took the loudness of a playground.

From a skipping rope
He took the length of the string,
He took the width of a pencil,
For his body.

Then his eyes glowed
He took the redness from Mars,
He took the gleam of the sea,
To make his eyes

And snake was born!

Danielle Ball (11)
Hatherton Lane Primary School

Fairground

Roller coasters twisting fast round the track,
Roller coasters zooming tightly with a crack.

Roller coasters swirling softly in the sky
Roller coasters whirling excitedly with a fly.

Ghost train turning swiftly on a spooky track,
Ghost train spinning smoothly with a crack.

Big wheel moving slowly through the trees,
Big wheel twirling so we can feel the breeze.

Louise Richards (9)
Hatherton Lane Primary School

Fairground

Teddy talking nicely in a stall
Teddy playing quietly at the door.
Teddy crying loudly, don't want more
Teddy crawling excitedly on the moon.

Roller coaster zooming fast on a track
Roller coaster moving sadly in a crack
Roller coaster whooshing happily in a back
Roller coaster swishing badly in the heat attack.

Ice cream drying slowly in the sun
Ice cream dripping nicely in the fun
Ice cream cooling happily in the tum
Ice cream melting badly, it tastes yum.

Emma Pringle (9)
Hatherton Lane Primary School

Fairground

Fairground crashing, echoing behind the trees
Fairground booming loudly in the breeze
Fairground clicking tightly on the grass
Fairground whooshing, slipping on the grass.

Roller coaster flying smoothly on the track
Roller coaster twisting rapidly
In the fashion that breaks my back.

Big wheel spinning fast above the ground
Big wheel halting slowly by the round
Big wheel slow inside the fairground
Big wheel zooming rapidly by a hound.

Ryan Bolstridge (8)
Hatherton Lane Primary School

Snake Began

Snake began
He took slime from the frog,
He took all colour out of the trees
And made his coat.

For his voice
He took the hissing of a kettle,
He took the quietness out of an empty room,
He took the whistle out of the wind.

He took the redness out of a red pencil,
He took the sight of an owl,
For his eyes.

He took a V letter,
He took a little red from the lizard,
To make his tongue.

Jack Healy (10)
Hatherton Lane Primary School

Fairground

Huge roller coaster zooming tightly above the water
Huge roller coaster twisting slowly at Mabel.

Huge roller coaster twirling fast in the sky
Huge roller coaster swirling nice, I can fly.

Funny people playing excitedly on the sand
Funny people shouting noisily at the band.

Funny people counting slowly, what fun
Funny people cooling nicely in the sun.

Ice cream melting silently in the sun
Ice cream cooling nicely in the fun.

Ice cream dripping silently in the heat
Ice cream standing quietly by my feet.

Charlotte Rutter (8)
Hatherton Lane Primary School

Winter's Here

Winter swayed,
up the shivering cliffs,
hanging icicles
off the high, gloomy rocks.

Winter danced,
through the winding trees,
making the leaves and webs
sparkle like diamonds
and then moved on.

Winter darted,
through the football pitch,
leaving the grass sparkling
like glitter
and then moved on.

Winter glided
on the shivering sea,
waves cooling rapidly.

Jade Mansell (11)
Hatherton Lane Primary School

Cat

He took the sharpness of a knife
Claws can save his life
Then he made his claws.

He took the twinkling of the stars
So he could see Mars
Then he made his eyes.

He took the fluff of a cloud
Of which he's very proud
Then he made his coat.

He creeps around
Without a sound
Then he made his movement.

Shannon Owen (10)
Hatherton Lane Primary School

Dog

Dog began
He took the thickness of a gorilla
He took the softness of a bunch of hair
And made his coat.

For his voice
He took the rumble of a volcano
He took the loudness of a playground
He took the screech of an owl.

From the wild
He took a bear's feet
He took the scratching of a lion
To make his paws.

Then dog
He took the tail of a monkey
He took the movement of a cheetah
To make his tail
And dog was born.

Stacey Sedgwick (10)
Hatherton Lane Primary School

Funny Jungle

Funny jungle noises,
Lions' silky hair,
Naughty baboons,
Orange quicksand,
Slippery, slimy ground,
Freezing cold river water,
Poisonous, colourful frogs,
Spiky berries,
Big green bushes,
Huge multicoloured oak trees.

Kimberly James (9)
Hatherton Lane Primary School

Dolphin Began

Dolphin began,
He took the shimmering of the sea,
He took the curves of the sun
And made his eyes.

For his body,
He took the streamline from an otter,
He took the length from a train,
He took the flexibility from a gymnast.

From branches,
He took the forks and twigs,
He took the flapping from a bird,
For his tail.

Then from a circle,
He took the shape of his fin,
He took the thickness of leather,
To make his skin.

And dolphin was born.

Jade Higgins (11)
Hatherton Lane Primary School

Lion Began

Lion began
He took the silence of a crocodile
He took the cunning of a fox
And made his stealth.

For his teeth
He took the sharpness of a dagger
He took the whiteness of snow
He took the points of a fork.

From a field
He took his fur from a rabbit
He took his colour of sand
To make his eyes.

Scott Lawton (11)
Hatherton Lane Primary School

Tiger Began

He took the stripes of a zebra,
He took the coat of a jaguar
And made his body.

For his attack,
He took the teeth of a lion,
He took the paws of a panther,
He took the strength of an elephant.

From the fox,
He took his slyness,
He took his stealth,
For his movement,

Then from the cat,
He took his sight,
He took his hearing,
To make his senses

And tiger was born.

Luke Bickley (11)
Hatherton Lane Primary School

Shopping Nonsense

I'm going to the shop
To get my mum a mop
Sugar over the floor
When I'm going out the door.

Having lollies
On the brollies
Babies crying
When they're lying.

My mum has got a deer
When I'm having beer
Time to go home
And look at my gnome.

Shannon O'Brien (8)
Hatherton Lane Primary School

Lion Began

He took the softness of a feather
He took the smoothness of silk
And made his mane.

For his tail
He took the length of a rope
He took the meander of the river
He took the width of a stick.

From a volcano
He took the rumble of the eruption
He took the roughness of the rock
For his roar.

Then from the circus
He took the slash of a whip
He took the point of a spear
To make his claws

And lion was made.

Joshua Smith (10)
Hatherton Lane Primary School

Beavers

Funny tail
Big teeth
Building dams across the river
Warning others by beating their tails
Working all day long
Biting wood
Very strong swimmers
Work in groups
Live in lodges
Very brave and skilful
Intelligent mammals.

Lewis Guttridge (9)
Hatherton Lane Primary School

Tiger Began

He took the thickness of foam
He took the smoothness of leather
And made his coat.

For his feet
He took the speed of a motorbike
He took the claws of a blade
He took the legs of a branch.

From the fair
He took the vibration of a bush
He took the colour of a ginger biscuit
For his tail.

Then the sound
He took the beat of music
He took the roaring of an earthquake
To make his voice

And tiger was born.

Thomas Williams (11)
Hatherton Lane Primary School

Fairground

Roller coaster winding tightly on the track
Roller coaster racing quickly above a crack
Roller coaster zooming hurriedly around the back
Roller coaster rushing fast, clickety-clack

Children waiting silently inside the shop
Children walking slowly next to a cop

Games booming loudly in the stall
Games scaring nastily inside the hall
Games moving weirdly on the wall
Games zooming quickly above the mall.

Courtney Green (9)
Hatherton Lane Primary School

Dog Began

Dog began
He took the softness of snow
He took the thickness of a duvet
And made his coat

For his eyes
He took the roundness of the sun
He took the blackness of the misty sky
He took the blue of the sea

From the fox
He took the pointed shape
He took the sharpness from the knife
For his teeth

He took the screech of an owl
He took the bang of a drum
To make his voice

And dog was born.

Amy Jones (11)
Hatherton Lane Primary School

Music

Playing the drum,
A big bang!
Having a sip of water,
A little ping,
A big guitar,
Flute whistling,
Violin playing,
Music gone wrong,
Dancing badly.

Ryan Stanley (8)
Hatherton Lane Primary School

Dolphin Began

He took the smoothness of glass
He took the colour of the sea
And made his body

For his fins
He took the spine of a fish
He took the curves of a winding river
He took the greyness of a misty day

He took the screech of an owl
He took the loudness of a human screaming
For is voice

Then from a human
He took good eyesight
He took the blueness from a pen
To make his eyes

And dolphin was born.

Jodie Butler (10)
Hatherton Lane Primary School

Funny Jungle

Silly jungle noises,
Lions' silky hair,
Wild animals,
Furry brown bears,
Very fast cheetahs,
Ice-cold river water,
Gungy quicksand,
Poisonous berries,
Huge green leaves,
And that is my jungle.

Charlotte Joseph (9)
Hatherton Lane Primary School

Holidays

Holidays are magic days
Golden beach where children play beach ball, sandcastles
and donkey rides
Jumping over waves, screaming cold or warm
Going on day trips to Blackpool or the airport
Driving to the massive water parks
When we get there we'll splash, slide and swim
Playing crazy golf with my mum, dad and brother
Looking in shops for clothes, jewellery or toys
Spending loads of my money on toys, buckets and spades
Having fun in the arcades
Until it's time to say bye-bye
It was lovely.

Laura Cox (9)
Hatherton Lane Primary School

Holiday, Holiday

Holiday, holiday
At the golden, sunny beach
Building super huge sandcastles
Splashing in the big blue waves
Palms swaying in the breeze
Holiday, holiday
Holiday, holiday
Seals splashing in the water
Riding cute brown donkeys
Climbing grassy green, rocky mountains
Excited about going to the carnival
Riding on a ghost train of tortures and terrors
Devon rabbits everywhere
Holiday, holiday
Can we go again?

Jordan Broomhall (8)
Hatherton Lane Primary School

The Lady Of Shalott

(Based on 'The Lady Of Shalott' by Alfred Lord Tennyson)

The castle stands at Camelot,
It has casement windows.
She sees a knight riding on a horse,
She moves away from the mirror.
The mirror starts to break.
The web falls out of the window, the knight's name is Sir Lancelot.
He wears armour, when the sun hits the armour it looks like it is on fire.
The Lady of Shalott wears robes. She looks in the mirror all day
and stays in the castle all day.
The many towered town is called Camelot.
She finds a boat, then she writes on the boat 'The Lady of Shalott'.
She sings until her blood freezes.
The field grows either side of the river,
Then the Lady of Shalott lies in the boat.
When the boat stops everyone sees her.
Even Sir Lancelot says a prayer to Jesus,
He says she has a beautiful face.
Look after her.

Gemma Hales (10)
Hatherton Lane Primary School

Dragons

Dragons live in holes
Dragons fly
Dragons eat human beings
Dragons run fast
Dragons breath fire
Dragons kick cats
Dragons have scary eyes
Dragons are spooky
Dragons always look after their slimy, muddy dens.

Matthew Instone (9)
Hatherton Lane Primary School

Jungle

In the spooky jungle
Elephants swinging their large, long grey trunks
Fierce swinging monkeys
Red and black mean, scary eyes,
Big brown bears always protecting their babies
Crocs snapping in the slimy water,
Small, fierce, buzzing bees,
Beautiful blue, smiling dolphins.

Chelsea Whitticase (8)
Hatherton Lane Primary School

Holidays

Lying on the golden beach,
    Swimming in the blue water,
Eating melting ice cream on the beach,
    Having swimming lessons in the hotel,
Eating a Sunday dinner in a restaurant,
    Going to have a massage in a salon,
Eating chips in a café,
    That's my favourite holiday.

Jodie Banks (9)
Hatherton Lane Primary School

Animals

Red foxes playing together,
Creeping, crying crododiles,
Brown, bouncy bears whistling,
Spiders making webs,
Butterflies sucking nectar,
Birds getting older,
Cats getting hungrier.

Luke Wilding (8)
Hatherton Lane Primary School

Killer Bats

Killer bats hanging in caves,
Spiders' webs and rats.
Killer bats eating rats,
Eating cats.
Strong wings and very black,
Only come out in the dark.
How scared, be prepared,
Wakes me up in the night.
What a fright!

Joshua Hartshorne (8)
Hatherton Lane Primary School

Holidays

On the go-karts, in the sea,
On the donkeys, on the beach.
In the pub eating ice cream,
Going shopping in the shop.
Being served, never stop,
Watching a film, lying down.
Playing games, on the sunbeds,
Time to go in the end, want to go again!

Tom Harding (8)
Hatherton Lane Primary School

Holidays

On the red and blue fast go-karts
Red and orange fire from a rocket roller coaster
In the white, quiet hotel
In the noisy shop
In the noisy club
On the big, sunny beach
In the deep blue sea.

Timmy Richards (9)
Hatherton Lane Primary School

Ghoul School

When we went to school
There was a ghostly ghoul
We jumped into the spooky pool
Then a plumber came with a tool
I shouted, 'Ghoul! Ghoul!'
We chased it over the water in the pool
Then he hid in the school.

Jordan Higgins (9)
Hatherton Lane Primary School

The Weather And Me

I was walking with my feet,
Down that frosty street,
Walking in the same beat,
In the wind my friends I meet.
Rain falling with a splash,
Cars might even crash.
The dustmen will take out the trash,
Hailstones falling with a dash.

Kayne Humphries (9)
Hatherton Lane Primary School

Snake

How do you slither?
When you slither you make me shiver
When I see you eat your dinner
You make me shiver
When you slither.

Jamie Garratley (9)
Hatherton Lane Primary School

Henry The Eighth

H enry was the king of England,
E very year or less you would have seen him with a wife,
N ever marry Henry or you would be executed,
R ather kind and powerful,
Y ou should get to know him,

T here is no one better than Henry,
H e was a perfect hunter,
E veryone watched him play tennis,

E ach day when Henry was young he liked to hunt,
I always beat people at jousting,
G reat at sport,
H enry was a liar to Anne Boleyn,
T he Church of England he created,
H e had a bad temper!

Abraham Gordon (8)
Lakeside Primary School

Jane Seymour

J ane Seymour was the only one who had a boy,
A nd she died a couple of weeks later,
N ever forgot Henry's love,
E dward was the child she had,

S eymour loved Henry a lot,
E verybody liked her,
Y ou should never normally
M arry Henry but she did,
O ctober 1537 she died,
U pset was Henry,
R eally sad.

Rosie Dudley (7)
Lakeside Primary School

Henry The Eighth

H enry first married Catherine of Aragon,
E njoyed playing tennis,
N ever milked a cow,
R ich, he spent it on expensive clothes,
Y ou wouldn't want to be his wife,

T wo of his wives were executed,
H enry was never alone,
E ach wife he married was scared of him,

E ach day Henry hunted,
I t was something he liked,
G ot loads of clothes,
H enry wanted a son,
T he only one he had was Edward,
H enry hated Anne of Cleves - she was ugly!

Daniel Eagleton (7)
Lakeside Primary School

Anne Boleyn

A nne had six fingers on one hand,
N ever had a son,
N ever had to do any work,
E xecuted on the 19th May,

B orn in Norfolk,
O nly one child,
L oved Henry lots,
E lizabeth, her daughter, became queen,
'Y ou have not given me a son,' said Henry,
'N ooo!' screamed Anne as the guillotine came down.

Daniel Bradley (8)
Lakeside Primary School

Henry The Eighth

H enry was rich,
E xecuted two of his wives,
N ever gave in at sport,
R eally wanted a son,
Y et only had one,

T oo clever for his opponents,
H e was naughty for chopping people's heads off,
E very wife wanted to give him a son to save their neck,

E dward was his first son,
I love somebody else was his excuse,
G ood at tennis, jousting and hunting,
H e was a powerful king
T oo good at getting new wives,
H enry was a great king,

Bethany Stokes (7)
Lakeside Primary School

Anne Of Cleves

A nne had a painting but when Henry saw it she was ugly,
N ever had a child with Henry,
N ow she is dead, she lived a long time ago,
E veryone said she should have stayed in Germany.

O verall she was the wife that Henry didn't want to marry,
F rom when she divorced Henry she lived in a house that
    he bought for her.

C leves was her last name,
L ove? Anne hated Henry,
E veryone said she was fat,
V ery good painting by Hans Holbein,
E nded up having a face only her mum liked,
S he divorced Henry the same year as marrying him.

Verity North (8)
Lakeside Primary School

Henry The Eighth

H e was rich,
E ach wife was scared of losing her head,
N ever did his own cooking,
R uled England,
Y elled at his second wife, Anne Boleyn,

T udor king,
H e gave a home to Anne of Cleves,
E ach time a lady came in he took off his hat,

E very day he went hunting,
I n Henry's church were loads of people,
G ot rid of Catherine Howard,
H e divorced two of his wives,
T he church was called the Church of England,
H e liked some of his wives.

Sam MacDonald (8)
Lakeside Primary School

Pizza And Chips Acrostic

P izza is yummy,
I ncredible flavours,
Z esty flavours,
Z aps you into another world,
A s tasty as anything.

A nd you have it with sweetcorn,
N aan bread with pizza, great!
D eliciously great.

C harming, chips are,
H eavenly tasty,
I ncredible value,
P erfect,
S picy, just made to go with pizzas!

Ellis Lucas (9)
Lakeside Primary School

My Little Cat Called Murphy

My little cat called Murphy,
Has the cutest little face,
A body that is black,
And a long black tail to chase.

His tongue is small and as rough as a wall,
And he has ears that prick up everywhere,
His eyes are glowing and black,
And he has sharp, white teeth in his jaw.

He loves to pounce and play with his toys,
And he also loves to sleep,
But his favourite thing he loves to do,
Is a game of hide-and-seek.

His claws are sharp and catchy,
And he's always been a pest,
But he's my little cat called Murphy,
Who is simply just the best.

Ciara Evans (10)
Lakeside Primary School

Ghost Train Acrostic

G host train is here,
H earing the screams of fear.
O ut and out, in and in as it goes,
S o watch out for your worst foes,
T ooting, tooting through the night.

T he ghost train is a terrible sight,
R un for your life its not a pretty sight.
A nd before you know it you have a fright,
I n the end people are left thinking it was a dream,
N ever will you see a ghost train again.

Cassie-Ann Smith (9)
Lakeside Primary School

I Wish . . .

I wish school was closed today,
So I could go out to play.
But there's work I need to finish today,
It needs to go up on display.

I wish school was shut today,
So I can stay in bed.
But I don't think Mmum would like that,
She'd pour water over my head.

I wish school was closed today,
So I can play with my toys.
My mum would be mad with me,
Because of all the noise.

Joseph Stevens (8)
Lakeside Primary School

Colours

What is red?
A fireman's head
What is green?
Grass in a dream
What is yellow?
A banana in a cello
What is blue?
A big kazoo
What is black?
A burger on a Big Mac
What is white?
A kite in daylight.

Matthew Dunn (11)
Lakeside Primary School

Old King Cole

Old King Cole played in goal
And a merry old soul was he
He said to Patrick, 'I scored a hat-trick
For you and for me.'

Ashley Williams (10)
Lakeside Primary School

Another Diamonte . . .

Cat
Vicious, energetic
Creeping, hunting, chasing
Scared its timid prey
Growling, purring, roaring
Fast, sly
Cheetah.

Nathan Garner (9)
Lakeside Primary School

Little Bo Peep

Little Bo Peep had no sheep to keep,
So she went off to see Humpty Dumpty.
She told him a joke,
He spilt his yolk,
And then became Empty Dumpty.

Amy Page (11)
Lakeside Primary School

Ghost In The School

S cary ghost in the school at night
C areful! Ghosts are in school
A nd scary all night
R un the ghosts are behind you
Y ou are scared.

Tristan Hughes (8)
Lakeside Primary School

Monster Diamonte

Beast
Smelly, sweaty
Slithering, slobbering, creeping
One eye bloodshot
Rolling, threatening, frightening
Torn clothes
Monster.

Andrew Bowering (9)
Lakeside Primary School

Frogs

F rogs are friendly.
R ough frogs are nasty.
O n your hands, frogs wee.
G round frogs are nice and soft.
S ome frogs play in water.

Natalie Lloyd (10)
Lakeside Primary School

My Horse (An Animal Diamonte)

Mammal
Lovely, soft
Galloping, watching, nuzzling
Plays happily all day
Spying, biting, running
Silky, shiny
Horse.

Alexandra Jackson (10)
Lakeside Primary School

Animal Diamonte . . .

Mammal,
Spiky, shy,
Curling, rolling, hiding,
Shuffles in the grass,
Freezing, stumbling, hunting,
Brown, black,
Hedgehog.

Jordan Evans (8)
Lakeside Primary School

Animal Diamonte

Insect,
Pretty, colourful,
Flying, floating, fluttering,
Dances merrily in the sunshine,
Playing, flying, dancing,
Thin, dry,
Butterfly.

Lauren Gibbons (8)
Lakeside Primary School

Dragons

D ead, you would be if you met one,
R ed flames they breathe,
A ll their scales shine,
G rinding their teeth for food,
O range flames in their eyes,
N asty bites they give you.

Sophie Wilson (9)
Lakeside Primary School

Animal Diamonte

Dog
Scary, furry
Running, hopping, jumping
Hunts food at night
Hiding, creeping, sleeping
Rough fur
Fox.

Kirsty Clarke (10)
Lakeside Primary School

This Is The Hand

This is the hand that opened the nut that went in my mouth
This is the hand that broke the window that smashed into pieces.
This is the hand that broke the orange and went in my house.
This is the hand that caught the thief in the house.

Eleanor Whitehouse (7)
Little Bloxwich CE Primary School

This Is The Hand

This is the hand
that felt the dog
that had a cough.

This is the hand
that grabbed the coat
that fell on the floor.

This is the hand
that shifted the bike
that broke down.

This is the hand
that peeled the apple
that was rotten.

Damon Cotton (8)
Little Bloxwich CE Primary School

Feet

Messy feet
Kicking in a park
Skinny feet
Dancing in a loud disco.

Spotty feet
Stamping on a sandy beach
Fatty feet
Bouncing on a large blue trampoline.

Thin feet
Jogging on a golden beach
Freckly feet
Bouncing on a soft bed.

Liam Christian (8)
Little Bloxwich CE Primary School

This Is The Hand

This is the hand
that waved the flag
and fell out of my hand.

This is the hand
that splashed my dog
that broke the bike
and never played.

This is the hand
that felt the cat
that got muddy.

This is the hand
that peeled a carrot
that didn't put the rubbish in the bin.

Jessica Jillian Price (7)
Little Bloxwich CE Primary School

Feet

Spotty feet
running in a black playground.
Hairy feet
walking in a huge park.
Smelly feet
hopping on a blue house.
Fat feet
bouncing on a large trampoline.
Skinny feet
jumping on a massive pogo stick,
Thin feet
kicking the toys in my room.

Ryan Parker (8)
Little Bloxwich CE Primary School

This Is The Hand

This is the hand
that rubbed the lamp
and a ghost came out.

This is the hand
that opened the door
for the teacher.

This is the hand
that caught the ball
and hurt my hand.

This is the hand
that broke the vase
and my mum went mad.

Charlotte Jackson (8)
Little Bloxwich CE Primary School

These Are The Feet

Blue feet
Kicking in soapy water
Spotty feet
Walk in a messy street.

Smelly feet
Running in a large park
Huge feet
Jumping in a funny house.

Skinny feet
Dancing in a loud disco
Pink feet
Leaping in the mud.

Gemma Greenwood (7)
Little Bloxwich CE Primary School

This Is The Hand

This is the hand
that waved goodbye
that played with his friend all day.

This is the hand
that helped his mum to hold a vase
that was smashed to pieces.

This is the hand
that opened a banana
that squashed it all up.

This is the hand
that caught the ball
that played every day.

Megan Chapman (7)
Little Bloxwich CE Primary School

Feet

Freckly feet
skating in a grassy park
Spotty feet
jumping on a blue pogo stick.

Large feet
kicking a white football
Thin feet
walking through a large laboratory.

Fat feet
running to a posh restaurant
Thin feet
skipping to a scruffy house.

Jack Hill (7)
Little Bloxwich CE Primary School

This Is The Hand

This is the hand
that rubbed his hands
by the fire.

This is the hand
that broke the bike
with its knife.

This is the hand
that grabbed the dog
that stroked him all day.

This is the hand
that shifted the sand
out of the box.

Rebecca Stringer (8)
Little Bloxwich CE Primary School

This Is The Hand

This is the hand
that helped the teacher
to lift the table

This is the hand
that grabbed the coat
that fell off a peg

This is the hand
that walked on his hands
and fell over

This is the hand
that put in the video
and switched it on.

Aidan Mansell (7)
Little Bloxwich CE Primary School

Feet

Hairy feet
running in a large park
Fat feet
paddling in deep sea

Freckly feet
jumping on a massive bed
Spotty feet
kicking on a small field.

Skinny feet
bouncing up and down on a trampoline
Huge feet
dancing at a dark disco.

Lauren Hunt (8)
Little Bloxwich CE Primary School

This Is The Hand

This is the hand
that grabbed the coat
that fell off the peg

This is the hand
that lifted the car
and couldn't let go

This is the hand
that grabbed the coat
and it didn't come off

This is the hand
that nicked a toy
and never gave it back.

Liam Froggatt (7)
Little Bloxwich CE Primary School

This Is The Hand

This is the hand
that grabbed the dog
that fell off the roof

This is the hand
that caught the dog
in his hands

This is the hand
that broke the aeroplane

This is the hand
that grabbed the coat
that fell off the peg.

Daniel Beale (7)
Little Bloxwich CE Primary School

Hand

This is the hand
that grabbed the coat
that fell off the peg

This is the hand
that clapped to the rhythm
that jumped to the beat

This is the hand
that made a cake
that splattered everywhere

This is the hand
that rubbed the feet
that smelt!

Chloe Harper (7)
Little Bloxwich CE Primary School

The Witch's Cat

The witch's cat, eyes as sparkling as marbles, fur nicely combed.
Prowling, while crawling up the wall - miaow, miaow.
Tail nicely *curled* then tail as straight as a ruler.
She jumps into a dustbin as *quick* as a flash catching a snack,
but what did she catch?
She *bounces* like someone on a trampoline, off the bin -
munch, munch, munch, she eats like a scavenger.
She eats the bunch while munch, munch, munch.
That's the witch's cat!

Navneet Budesha (10)
Little Bloxwich CE Primary School

A Witch's Cat

As the witch's cat plodded,
I recognised its eyes were as green as emeralds,
Its fur as black as a crow.
So furious, its back arched up.
The cat's head whipped round as it growled as ferocious
As a mountain lion.
It smiled scarily with teeth as sharp as needles.

Luke Clark (9)
Little Bloxwich CE Primary School

The Snake!

There was a snake as brown as soil,
His skin was as smooth as ice,
Every day he used to slither slowly in the grass,
His eyes were as black as the dots on a Dalmatian,
Moving as slow as a tortoise,
The snake was as dangerous as poison!

Tom Burden (10)
Little Bloxwich CE Primary School

The Witch's Cat

Eyes as green as emeralds,
Fur as black as a bat,
That's the witch's cat.

Whiskers as straight as rulers,
Fur as scruffy as an old mat,
That's the witch's cat.

Teeth as sharp as thorns,
Claws as pointy as forks,
That's the witch's cat.

Reanne Simone Langston (10)
Little Bloxwich CE Primary School

Pond

A pond as dark as the graveyard on a winter's night.
Beautiful colours darting around.
Grasses growing as tall as a haunted house.
Lily pads as big as a black door in the wall of a church.

Thomas Pritchard (9)
Little Bloxwich CE Primary School

Magic Cat

He crept along the drainpipe,
As skilful as a gymnast,
When he saw me,
He ran off as fast as a motorbike,
Now that's fast!
He ran over to me,
His eyes were something to see,
They were like emeralds gleaming,
I really thought I was dreaming!
It must have been a witch's cat to look like that.

Katie Richards (10)
Little Bloxwich CE Primary School

The Witch's Cat

Whiskers, whiskers, whiskers,
Mouth as large as a folder,
Teeth as sparkling as the moon in the night sky,
Walking along the garden wall as silent as a grave,
As evil as a dinosaur,
Eyes shining like baubles on a Christmas tree,
Claws as sharp as stones,
Tail as straight as a pencil.

Alysha Harris (10)
Little Bloxwich CE Primary School

The Cat

The green eyes glaring, staring at me,
Its teeth as sharp as a thorn,
'Go! Go! Run!' I shouted.
Its eyes as big as saucepans,
And as green as emeralds,
Its tail as big as a banana.

Stephen Witton (10)
Little Bloxwich CE Primary School

Mad Cat

As angry as fire flaming hot fur
As fierce as a bear, can you hear it roar?
As hungry as a lion chewing on meat
As loud as a gun blasting through a wall.

Guy Buchanan (10)
Little Bloxwich CE Primary School

The Cat

Sparkling eyes that look like emeralds,
Shining in the dark sky.
Its back is arched like an entrance to a castle,
When it gets ready to sprint at its prey.
It's as silent as a graveyard.
Its tail is as white as a polar bear.

Oliver Chapman (9)
Little Bloxwich CE Primary School

The Witch's Cat

He crept in the garden
With green emerald eyes
Staring at me
With razor sharp claws
Scratching up the door
Eyes as big as saucepans
Silent as the breeze in the air.

Thomas Spencer (10)
Little Bloxwich CE Primary School

My Pet Cat

Eyes like baubles on a Christmas tree when she walks past.
When she walks in the dark hall her tail is as straight as a broomstick.
She is black as the night sky.
Her claws are as sharp as thorns.

Rebecca Dennis (10)
Little Bloxwich CE Primary School

The Witch's Cat

Its tail is like a broomstick swaying from side to side
Its back is like the entrance to a castle, waiting to be opened
Its eyes are like lemons staring out of the grass
Its fur is as black as a crow
Its hands are as rough as sandpaper rubbing on wood.

Samuel Hubble (9)
Little Bloxwich CE Primary School

The Witch's Cat

It's looking at me,
With its eyes as bright as a light bulb,
Sparkling like stars,
Walking on the wall like a tight rope walker,
Never falling off,
His fur as black as the night sky,
His claws as sharp as thorns.

Emily Pearce (9)
Little Bloxwich CE Primary School

My Mum

She is a cosy bed
She is a lively monkey
She is a noisy supermarket
She is a loud school bell
She is teatime, busy
That's my mum.

Elizabeth Dennis (10)
Little Bloxwich CE Primary School

Snake

The snake with his forked tongue
And his black, beady eyes
He slithers through the grass
As quiet as a room at night
As he goes and hunts his prey.

Joshua Reynolds (9)
Little Bloxwich CE Primary School

The Cat

Creeps along the wall as silent as a dark alley
Fur dark as a pitch-black night
Eyes as yellow as lemons staring at the wall
Running as fast as a racing car
As silent as a little breeze.

Luke Povey (10)
Little Bloxwich CE Primary School

My Mum

She is a cosy bed
She is a kind cat
She is a quiet, busy classroom
She is a humming bee
She is bedtime, peace and quiet
That's my mum.

Sophie James (9)
Little Bloxwich CE Primary School

The Witch's Cat

Bright yellow eyes that look like lemons in the sun,
Hissing at me like it's about to attack, oh no!
With fur as black as a midnight sky,
Glaring at me with beady eyes,
Camouflaged fur because it's very late,
Pouncing like a jumping frog,
It's racing over to me!
Argh!

Natalie Danielle Neale (10)
Little Bloxwich CE Primary School

This Is The Hand

This is the hand
that felt the dog
because it looked cuddly.

This is the hand
that helped the man
to put the table back.

This is the hand
that picked some sweets
because it was hungry.

Jessica Hancox (8)
Little Bloxwich CE Primary School

My Rabbits

R unning and hopping all day long
A pproaches for the carrots
B ouncing up and down
B unnies, bunnies, fluffy bunnies
I n their lovely huts
T iny toes jumping up and down.

Zobia Kausar (10)
Lodge CP School

The Eiffel Tower

The Eiffel Tower,
Built to reach the sky,
Beautiful, wonderful, very high,
Like a giant reaching for the sky.
Like being on top of the world
It makes us feel like kings and queens,
Like wonderful bees buzzing around,
The Eiffel Tower,
It reminds us how enjoyable life is!

Amina Khanom (10)
Lodge CP School

Daisy, Daisy

Daisies are beautiful,
Shining like the golden sun.
When people step on them,
They just want to run.
'What are you doing?'
Said the trodden-on daisy,
'You are so big,
I can't believe you are so lazy!'

Sarah Ali (9)
Lodge CP School

The Lily

The lily has its shiny glow
Its petals are as silky as snow.
Lily, lily, your beauty shows through,
Lily, lily, I love you.
Your colours are white and yellow
And you're such a happy fellow.

Samantha Gill (9)
Lodge CP School

Detention!

We walked into the classroom
With our hands behind our backs.
He said, 'Prepare to meet your doom,'
And he searched our slacks.

We sat down at our tables
And looked up at the ceiling.
He gave us each sticky labels,
And we caught a nasty feeling.

We all looked at the teacher,
He bawled, 'Write down your names.'
He then drew a funny picture
Which said there will be no games.

An hour or so had passed,
The detention bell had rung.
'You'd all better go real fast,'
He said, as he sat down with a bang.

Briony Scarlett (11)
Lodge CP School

Walking On The Moon

Slowly as I walk on the surface of the moon,
As I started to sprint across my room.

While I get floating system in a groove,
Then I start to get the move.

I find a moon rock
That has the smell of a smelly sock.

Then I see some stars,
I imagine I'm on Mars.

I feel a tingling in my toes
Now I have to go, but here is a moon pose.

Amardeep Kaur (11)
Lodge CP School

The Worst Crime!

I'd rather say it as a rhyme,
My friend did the worst ever crime.
He went up to the teacher,
Showed a creepy creature.
It went up her shirt,
Glad it didn't go up her skirt!
The teacher sent him to the Head,
Man! He's gonna be dead!

The next day the teacher was a zombie,
She came up and stood right next to me.
As if it was a horrid curse
I could see her temper immerse.
She asked me where's my mate,
You should have seen her state.
She had a gulp of water from her glass,
And carried on teaching the class.

And from that night,
She was never seen in sight!

Abdullah Choudhury (10)
Lodge CP School

My Moon Poem

While I'm walking on the surface of the moon
I feel excited, but very odd.
I'm moving very slowly on the surface of the moon.
I see the sparkling stars floating about just like me.
If you see the Earth from up here, it looks amazing.
A chill just ran down my spine.
What's that lurking about?
I think it's an alien.
Watch out! Watch out! Watch out!

Sonia Suman (11)
Lodge CP School

Autumn

Crispy leaves upon the ground,
Crunch, crunch, not much of a sound.
Throw me up into the sky,
Then back down I will fly.
The breeze pushes me side to side,
On a different surface now I'll glide.
Soon be cold, I'll begin to die,
I'll come back, no need to sigh.
I'm never attached to any laces,
But I'll tell you a fact, we go our own paces.
Leaves are different sizes and shapes,
Can't walk, not able to wear capes.
Everywhere we are scattered,
Sometimes we'll be absolutely flattered.

Fauzia Jabeen (10)
Lodge CP School

The Yellow Poem

Yellow is a flower like the sun up in the sky,
I look at the sunshine and see the birds fly.
Yellow makes me happy, it makes everybody friends,
Yellow is a great big Mercedes Benz.

Vanilla ice cream is yellow,
Make sure you say, 'Hello!'
I see the yellow stars,
They look like some bright cars,
But when it becomes night,
Don't let it out of your sight.

Nurjahan Aktar (8)
Lodge CP School

The Yellow Poem

Yellow is a runny egg to dip your chips into,
Yellow is the lemon I drink for my flu,
Yellow makes me happy, it makes my smile so bright,
Yellow is my ice cream and the stars at night.
Yellow is a light, it makes my eyes water,
Yellow is the hat I bought for my daughter.
Yellow is a sunflower in my garden,
It grows so high into the sky,
Yellow makes me cheerful, I feel so glad,
Yellow never ever makes me sad.

Shelina Hussain (7)
Lodge CP School

Colours

Imagine a world full of colour.
Beauty of colour comes in different forms,
Added with different shapes and sizes,
Overflowing with colour, draining to another
Splash of colour on a rainbow flower,
Standing tall and proud in this world
Of wonderful colour draining into one another.

Shaheen Malik (11)
Lodge CP School

The Stars That Live Beyond

I want to ride the stars
On a rocket to Mars.
I love the stars, and I did see Mars!
The stars are cool, they are so small.
I wish they were mine
Because they are so fine.
They come out at night
And shine like the moon.

Jaya Chohan (8)
Lodge CP School

My Whopping Family

My dad's one chappy,
My brother wears nappies,
My sister's a hippy,
My cousin is flippy,
My uncle loves football,
My auntie's name is Paul.

My whopping family,
My crazy family,
My weird family,
My mad family,
My whopping family!

My grandfather's dead,
My mummy's in bed,
My uncle loves slugs,
My cousin eats bugs,
My sister spends money
And I love honey.

My whopping family,
My crazy family,
My weird family,
My mad family,
My whopping family!

Humayra Kamal (9)
Lodge CP School

School

S aturday, Sunday, hooray, no school
C ream custard pies at home
H istory, geography, not for me
O h no, I hate Mondays
O K, it's not too bad
L earning all day I get tired.

Kiran Balaggan (10)
Lodge CP School

Once Upon a Rhyme

O ctopus have beautiful skin,
N ature is all animals love.
C heetahs love running,
E lephants have big trunks.

U nder the trees, monkeys sit,
P igs are pink.
O val-shaped eyes has a dog.
N ature has fresh air and flowers.

A nts are small.

R hinos are tough,
H ares run slow,
Y aks smell nasty,
M onkeys eat bananas,
E lephants drink clean water.

Gagandeep Dhillon (10)
Lodge CP School

Reach Up To The Sky

Reach up, reach up,
Fly and reach up with your hand
In the sky.
When your hands are in the sky,
You can feel the clouds passing by.
It becomes night, the moon is shining bright,
The stars are cold like ice.
I wish you were here now,
Flying through the night.

Priya Balagan (7)
Lodge CP School

Friendship

Written with a pen,
Sealed with a kiss,
If you are my friend, then answer this,
Are we friends or are we not?
You told me once but I forgot.
So tell me now and tell me true,
So I can say I'm here for you.
Of all the friends I've ever met,
You're the one I'll never forget.
And if I die before you do,
I'll go to Heaven and wait for you,
I'll give the angels back their wings.
Of all the friends I've met,
You're the one I'll never forget.

Asimah Kauser (10)
Lodge CP School

Friends Forever

B ringing happiness to one another
E very day telling secrets
S miling at each other every day
T reating each other with respect

F riends, friends, friends
R especting each other
I 'll always be by your side
E nding with a lovely day
N o one will come between us
D oing all sorts of things together
S ticking up for one another.

Anisa Akhtar (10)
Lodge CP School

Tiger

T iger, tiger, I'm scared of you,
I 'm hungry, I bet you are too,
G etting zebras for your tea
E veryone run to the tree
R oar, roar, roar, he's coming now.
    One, two three, he's got me, *ow!*

Habiba Begum (10)
Lodge CP School

Snacks

If rain was chocolate, I would bring down showers,
If sweets were seconds, I'd have hours.
If a wave was gum, I'd have a sea,
If snacks were people, I'd eat Lee.
These are just 'ifs', it will never come real,
Now I'll go and eat and ordinary meal.

Yahya Saeed (10)
Lodge CP School

My Dream Car Haiku

In your fast dream car
Hurtling down the motorway
City lights flash by.

Ravinder Deol (10)
Lodge CP School

Rugby

The scrum is over,
Out comes the ball with a tornado spin.
Down the line it goes.
Tactics going to plan, switches going in and out.
The ball is at the wing, with the man running fast,
Mud lapping his boots.
Cheering from the crowd.
Try.

Benjamin Wheeler (11)
Mayfield Preparatory School

Night And Day

The sun sets while the sea rests
And a gentle breeze on the night's cool seas,
Then soon the moonlight shone
And a gust of wind approached,
And howling could be heard from the distant trees.

The sun rises while the moon goes
And a gentle morning breeze on the day's cool seas,
Then soon the sunlight shone and
A gust of wind approached,
And whistling birds could be heard from the distant trees.

Sukhpreet Dosanjh (10)
Mayfield Preparatory School

The Cheetah

Its erect ears and its prowling eyes
Search for its prey in an endless disguise.

Its long, sleek body, ready to punch,
When an innocent creature reveals itself.

Out of the long grass, the cheetah will dart
And insert its jaw in the creature's heart.

Olivia Ireson (11)
Mayfield Preparatory School

The Eagle

He swoops and dives, on tender wing,
A floating figure, hovering above the valley floor,
Scanning every tree and every thread
Of the pine-needle carpet below,
Where many a rabbit or mouse,
Concealed beneath this prickly blanket,
Falls silent and turns a fearful eye towards the trembling sky.
And they are there no more.

He swoops and dives, a floating figure
Hovering below the azure, mountain sky,
And with trembling eye, catches sight of a young rabbit
Flitting through the bushes nearby.
Unsure, he gazes upwards,
To see Mother Nature with her back turned,
Idly talking to her son, the sky,
Then dives with quivering talons
And snatches what he believes is his share of nature,
And with a screech of triumph,
Returns swiftly to his mountain eyrie.

And when settled in his eyrie and
His chirping eaglets and wife have been fed
So that they are satisfied,
He alone, on fluttering wings, swoops to the peak of the mountain
And eats his portion of the hunt,
Savouring the succulent flavour of the rabbit.
However, he never thought about the value of the rabbit's life,
Or that a lifetime's chance
Had been destroyed by one hour's labour.

Charles Isherwood (11)
Mayfield Preparatory School

The Sun

The sunrise awakens the darting birds,
The butterflies dance by the burning sun,
The heavy winds blow through the delicate tree branches,
The caterpillars wriggle through the sweet-scented dew.

The river sparkles and glistens in the sun,
And ripples stir the calm blue water.
With daisies and buttercups growing in meadows,
Tulips and bluebells too.

But the day is over so fast, so fast,
And the woods are darkened at night,
The sun sets, the full moon rises,
The moon cornered by stormy clouds.

The plants all droop and bow their heads,
The eerie smell of danger hangs in the air.
Mysterious creatures slink around,
Making faint shadows that flicker.

The river is long and slender and black,
And clouds of blood rise from the bed.
The trees are swaying, bare and white,
And they grab you if you pass.

Everything that was once living is now dying,
Everything so dull and lifeless.
But everything is waiting, waiting,
Simply waiting for the sun.

Navreen Mangat (10)
Mayfield Preparatory School

Fish At Sea

A shoal of fish set out to sea,
What is to be? What is to be?
Looking for a place to be free,
What is to be? What is to be?

They hear the snap of lively jaws,
They are unsure. They are unsure.
A shark nearby has taken four,
No longer unsure. No longer unsure.

They hear the sound of a bullhorn,
They are unsure. They are unsure.
A fishing boat takes another four,
No longer unsure. No longer unsure.

They hear what sounds like a loud groan,
They are unsure. They are unsure.
A whale has taken another four,
No longer unsure. No longer unsure.

Only one remains of the shoal,
All alone. All alone.
Remembers the fishes of the shoal,
All alone. All alone.

Madhav Bakshi (10)
Mayfield Preparatory School

The Cellar

I go down to the cellar
To the pitch blackness,
To the quiet empty space,
And it is really scary.
No one goes down the cellar except for me.

Manveer Mahal (10)
Mayfield Preparatory School

Four Seasons

Winter brings us cold and frost,
Warmer weather has now been lost.
Slippery pavements where we lose our tread,
Oh! The season to stay in bed!

Autumn sees the trees so bare,
Leaves blow down without a care.
Nights draw in so very fast,
I wish the summer would always last.

Spring sees the flowers in full bloom,
Tulips and daffodils in people's front rooms.
The weather improves for better times ahead,
Those dark days of winter are now truly dead.

Summer is the most perfect time,
Warmth and holidays put us all in our prime.
The days are long and filled with fun,
At the end of the season, my playtime is done.

Elisha Edgeworth (10)
Mayfield Preparatory School

The Wind

The wind, it howls through the open air,
Slicing through stillness, like a fiendish nightmare.
Older than the world and harder than steel,
Death be upon the one who feels
Its mighty wrath, to its full extent.
Like a legion of lions, without relent.
Twisting apart mighty oaks in the night
And all that remains, fears in the night
Of this devilish fiend, ruler of chaos,
Wreaker of havoc, who plunders this world,
And those who oppose him shall discover
The true meaning of eternal slumber.

Colin Hock (10)
Mayfield Preparatory School

Dolphins At Sea

Far out on the distant horizon,
Where the sun set
On the crystal clear, blue ocean,
What do I see?
Bottle-nosed dolphins jumping, dancing,
Diving, gliding
Through the waves.

The pod of dolphins swimming together,
Communicating by secret radar,
They live free and happy lives
In the deep, clean, sparkling seas,
Darting amongst the coral reefs.

Long may this be so!

Alice Holtom (10)
Mayfield Preparatory School

The Sea

The sea is a snake,
Giant and blue,
Swirling and whirling across the beach
All day through.

But at the beauty of midday,
Upon the rocky shores,
The roaring of the sea
Leaps forward with its dusty paws.

And at night
It calms down
Into eeriness,
A sleeping gown.

Mahima Kharabanda (10)
Mayfield Preparatory School

Sea

Let me tell you about the mysterious sea,
It draws me to its shore.
The waves crash down as the sun comes up
And leave me wanting more.
The sand is silky and soft to touch,
It soon engulfs my feet.
As I look out over the horizon,
The land and sea will meet.
The shells are bright, the stones are smooth,
The seaweed crawls along,
The footprints appear and then they go
With the waves as they join in their song.
In the watery grave of the sailors and ships,
The sharks are desperate for prey.
The merpeople guide the travellers through
For a safe, non-threatening way.
The sea makes me calm and at peace with the world,
All my troubles just fly away.
It's a real miracle that it will ebb and flow,
Through the night and all through the day.

Philippa Mills (10)
Mayfield Preparatory School

Red

The colour of fire burning bright,
A field of poppies - what a sight!
The kit of Man United, Liverpool too,
A Livingstone tie, as good as new.
A strawberry is a delicious fruit,
A London bus on many a red route.
The ruby is a precious stone,
A rose given - you're not alone.
Lava, the tears that volcanoes shed,
I really love the colour red!

Ben Watson (10)
Mayfield Preparatory School

Ghosts

The ghosts were roaming in the night,
Haunting, scaring, leaving a fright.
Blood was falling from the walls,
Blood was falling down the roads.

At 12 o'clock the wind blows high,
When all the spirits go up in the sky.
As the clouds gather, they go dark and cry.
As the humans lie, the ghosts die.

Anjali Parekh (11)
Mayfield Preparatory School

The Sky And The Sea

The dark blue sea
Darkens every time the rain falls.
The sky is black at night,
And in the sea,
Nothing becomes white.

Shamail Khan (11)
Mayfield Preparatory School

Animals

The snake slithers across the sandy shores,
The bear wanders the forests,
The shark swims all alone in the dark
And the lion roars in the jungle.
And man evolves from apes.

Natasha Patel (11)
Mayfield Preparatory School

Black

As black as coal
As black as the night sky
As black as blackberries
As black as pepper
As black as dark corners in bad times
As black as tar before use
As black as the bottom of the ocean
As black as a shining mare
Petals of black give blisters
Of an ongoing pain.

Raman Sidhu (9)
Mayfield Preparatory School

What's White?

My PE shorts, my shirt,
Cotton wool clouds filled with snow,
Sugar icing on a birthday cake,
Daisies, snowdrops, crocuses and cuckoo spit,
The froth of waves in a foamy sea,
Doves, polar bears and a computer mouse,
This paper.

Thomas Greatrex (9)
Mayfield Preparatory School

Red

Red is the colour of the sunset,
Red is the colour of blood,
Red is the colour of love and heart,
Red is hate and anger,
Red is strawberry.

Nika Norman (9)
Mayfield Preparatory School

Red

The heart of a person is red,
The rosy cheeks on a person are red,
The blood of a person is red,
The sunrise that rises is red,
The heartbeat of everyone is loud and red,
The roses in the garden are red,
The ladybirds that fly are red,
The anger on someone's face is red,
The strawberry that you eat is red,
And Hell underneath is also red.
The jam that you put on your toast is red,
The ruby that you put on your finger is red,
The robe of a king is bright, bright red.
The lava from the fire is burning red,
The nail varnish that you wear is red,
The warmth from your house is a happy red,
And the telephone box that you phone from
Is red as red could be!

Jasdeep Bath (10)
Mayfield Preparatory School

Night

The air is silent,
And high above the ground
The black night sky covers like a tent.
Not hearing a sound
The moon floats by,
While its face looks down
From the twinkling sky.
As people doze in the sleepy town,
In the cloudless sky, the stars
Sparkle like dazzling diamonds,
As though they are fragments of Mars
Reflected in a shimmering pond.

Laura Marshall (11)
Mayfield Preparatory School

White

White is a cloudy sky,
Which holds clouds
Of pure white snow.
It drops like truth.
As it drops, it becomes
A white blanket.

White is a snow-covered iceberg
On a frozen lake.
White is a polar bear
Walking in the pure white Arctic
Covered in pure white snow.
White is a pure white swan,
Gliding below the cloudy sky.

White is as pure as truth.

Emily Ratcliffe (9)
Mayfield Preparatory School

Blue

Blue is the winding stream
That runs through a clump of trees,
The colour of icicles that glisten
And stab the air.
Blue is the morning on a winter's day,
And you can hear it in the wind.
Blue is the sky
Without a puffy cloud in sight.
It's a feeling to be sad and down.
Blue is heaven, I must say,
Blue is the colour of the world
Where everyone is different.

Amrita Dhallu (10)
Mayfield Preparatory School

Apokobide Is Near

In an old ruin lived a monster,
Packed with horror and loneliness.
On a cold winter's night he crept out,
Kidnapping the cold from the icicles.
Over the snow he crept, looking for something to eat.
Baffled where to look, he found something,
Identity like a ball of snow,
Dead almost of the cold,
Encased in a furry skin, the mouse slept
At the bottom of the food chain.

Abigail Higginbottom (9)
Mayfield Preparatory School

Red

Red is the colour of anger and rage,
Red is the colour of hunting wear,
Red is the colour of a thumping heart,
Red is the crackling fire,
Red is the colour of wine,
Red is the colour of the sunset,
Red is blood,
Red is the rose of love.

Jasmehar Mavi (9)
Mayfield Preparatory School

Black

Black is the midnight sky
And lipstick you put on your lips.
Black is your hair which shines in the light.
Black is space with sparkling stars in the air,
And black is a frightening coldness,
Making goosebumps.

Rishika Patel (9)
Mayfield Preparatory School

Orange

Orange is the midsummer sky,
Orange is the burning flame
And the tropics.
It's the succulent satsuma
And the mellow mango,
Or the falling leaves of autumn,
And, as many agree,
It's the tremendous tiger,
And it's as old as amber.

Matthew Fielden (9)
Mayfield Preparatory School

Green

Green is the colour of the countryside,
Fields full of fresh green grass,
Peaceful, tranquil and cool,
Too good to spoil,
Spring brings fresh new life.
The seashore awash with green seaweed.
Green is the colour of envy,
Flashing green emeralds.
Green is the colour of the world.

Bethany Marshall (9)
Mayfield Preparatory School

Red

Red is a juicy strawberry
And a summer sunset,
And the raging anger of someone upset.
Red is burning lava
And the roaring flames of a fire.

Charlotte Underhill (9)
Mayfield Preparatory School

Gold

Cockerel crowing,
Sun glowing,
Everyone is having lots of fun
Being in the golden sun.

Golden, golden, golden and bright,
Shine your light,
Shine your light.

Cockerel crowing,
Sun glowing,
Everyone loves your golden essence.
Everyone wants to be in your presence.

Golden, golden, golden and bright,
Shine your light,
Shine your light.

Japjeet Kulair (9)
Mayfield Preparatory School

Red

Red is the colour of love,
Not the colour of a dove.
To you and me,
The colour of apples in a tree.

Red is the colour of hearts,
Envelopes with love letters inside.
'Dear Darling,' they read.

Red is the colour of blood,
When your finger is pricked by a rose.
And last of all,
Red is the colour of a robin's breast.

Melissa Kirkland-Swann (10)
Mayfield Preparatory School

Green

Green is the colour of nature,
Of grass and leaves.
It is the colour of envy.
Green is the green alligator
In the green jungle on green, green Earth.
Green is the colour of emerald,
So precious and rare.
It is the colour of fruit,
Apples, grapes, pears
And sometimes bananas.
Green is the colour of the German football kit,
Never victorious.

Chandon Chahal (10)
Mayfield Preparatory School

Red

Red is the pride
Of England's rose
And the dark pits
Of Hell.
Red is the anger
That rages inside
When things aren't
Going your way.
Red is the blush
Of harvest's first apple
And the colour
Of strawberry jam.

Jonathan Mahon (10)
Mayfield Preparatory School

Green

Nature's green, the finest thing I've seen!
Green is an emerald ring,
A precious gift that someone could bring!
And poison ivy is green,
Oh, and pears,
But not all good things are green.
Envy is green,
And a crocodile is green,
And it's the scariest thing I've seen!

Sara Farooqui (10)
Mayfield Preparatory School

Red

Red is the colour of breaking dawn
And Manchester United,
Livingstone are red,
Apples are shining red,
Blood is red.
Red is the colour of the Chinese flag.
A cricket ball is red.
Red is the colour of your heart and love.

Arjan Drayton-Chana (9)
Mayfield Preparatory School

Red

Red is the colour of the sunset,
Warm, sunny and kind.
Red is the blood of anger,
And love of a true heart.
Love and anger will never end.

Ashveen Kohli (9)
Mayfield Preparatory School

Sun

Slowly, silently, rises the sun,
Walks the morning, the day has come.
This way and that she peers and sees
Golden leaves upon golden trees.
Sits by the door like a log,
With paws of gold barks the dog.
In the sky she glows and glows,
But moves slow and slow to flow.
By the window you see some rays,
They're so beautiful you have to stay,
And the bees hum in the sun,
But finish when the day is done.

Adam Patel (8)
Mayfield Preparatory School

Gold

Slowly, silently, now the sun
Lights the countries one by one.
Slowly now, she rises proud
Over golden fruit and golden cloud.
One by one the gold eggs hatch,
Resting on the golden branch.

Philippa Southern (9)
Mayfield Preparatory School

Gold

Slowly, silently, now the sun
Walks the day now the moon is done.
This way and that she peers and sees
Golden fruit upon golden trees.
With paws of gold sleeps the cat
Peacefully purring on the mat.

Emma Barker (8)
Mayfield Preparatory School

Golden

Slowly, silently, now the sun
Walks the day, now night is done.
This way and that, she peers and sees
Golden fruit upon golden trees.
Now the sun shines upon the stream,
Floating in a golden dream.
Now the sun shines on golden lilies
As a mouse nibbles on cheese.

Gavan Nijjar (8)
Mayfield Preparatory School

Gold

Rising early, now the sun
Lifts the day now night has done.
This way and that, she peers and sees
Golden bees near golden trees.
One by one the windows gleam,
Catching her rays, the golden stream.
The cats come home
Now the night's done.

Shannon Chatha (8)
Mayfield Preparatory School

Gold

Rising silently, now the sun
Walks the day, now night is done.
This way and that, she looks and spies
Golden clouds in the golden skies.
The blackbird sings, while the cockerels crow,
While the river does gently flow.
The sun shines on the golden dogs,
While they chase the golden logs.

Richard Ng (8)
Mayfield Preparatory School

Gold

Morning has broken,
The cockerel crows
In the golden sunshine.
The spider makes his web
While the sun shines brightly,
New flowers start to open
And golden fruits grow ripely.
The blackbird sings a jolly song
And the postman delivers his post,
While the dog barks at him in the sun.

Jagveer Mahal (9)
Mayfield Preparatory School

Gold

Slowly, silently, now the sun
Wakes the morning in her golden gown.
This way and that she peers and sees
New life on the breeze.
The nectar that the bees take
Is on the breakfast tray.

Miles Carlisle (8)
Mayfield Preparatory School

Gold

The gold sun rises when the silver moon falls,
Cats return to their owners, when they eat their daily dish.
The dogs bark at the postman,
And the fish wake from their dead-like sleep.
Children fall out of bed when mums say, 'Breakfast,'
And the cockerel crows to make sure everyone's awake.

Jonathan Duckett (9)
Mayfield Preparatory School

Golden

Slowly, silently,
Now the sun
Walks the day,
Now dark has gone.
This way and that
She peers and sees
With her golden gown
A golden dream
Floating in the stream.

Robert Angell (9)
Mayfield Preparatory School

Sun

Slowly, silently the sun
Walks the morning -
The day has come.
People are washing,
The milkman comes -
Milk for the breakfast table.

Jordon Sproule (8)
Mayfield Preparatory School

Gold

Slowly, silently, up rises the sun,
Lighting up streams one by one.
Here crows the cockerel on the weathervane,
Waking up people on the country lane.

Virron Chahal (8)
Mayfield Preparatory School

Gold

Golden, golden is the sun,
Now the night is done.
The cockerel crows,
It's such a way
To wake up and see the golden sun.

Philippa Watson (8)
Mayfield Preparatory School

Animal Haikus

A silly tabby
With a rumbling stomach
With a screeching paw!

Tabby is ginger,
He used to live in Moxly,
It's a tabby cat!

Abigail Page (10)
Rough Hay Primary School

Panda Haikus

Panda eats bamboo
That lives in the big forest
Black and white panda.

Climbing up a tree,
Drinking water from a pot,
Might be wild, but cute!

Sandeep Sandhu (11)
Rough Hay Primary School

Animal Haikus

Sitting on a tree,
Round and orange like a ball,
An orang-utan!

An orange colour,
With a round and fat belly
Eating bananas!

Tanjina Ali (11)
Rough Hay Primary School

Dogs Haikus

My puppy is small,
He loves to eat Pedigree,
He sleeps all day long.

We love him a lot,
He is the best dog ever,
But he sleeps a lot!

Martin Rollason (11)
Rough Hay Primary School

Tiger Haikus

Ready for dinner!
A sneaky, lazy tiger,
A tiger, beware!

It is behind you,
Do not move, it wants its prey,
Licking its big lips!

Mark Kendall (11)
Rough Hay Primary School

Killer Whale Haikus

Big black killer whale
That lives in a blue ocean
Eats tiny fishes!

Most are black and white
Squirting water all day long,
When it comes to dawn.

Carol Brooks (11)
Rough Hay Primary School

Dodo Haikus

Dodo, fat and plump
Soon goes up and soon comes down,
Hunted till no more.

Feathery creatures,
Extinct lots of years ago,
Now they have all gone.

Ryce Duffus (10)
Rough Hay Primary School

Caterpillar Haikus

The caterpillar
Turned into a butterfly,
He flutters all day.

His small little wings
Have multicoloured patterns,
He won't live for long.

Gemma Hayward (11)
Rough Hay Primary School

Pandas Haikus

White, black and furry,
And also wild and giant,
Big or small they're cute!

Pandas are lovely,
Their cubs are so very cute,
White and furry bears!

Deanna Banks (10)
Rough Hay Primary School

A Lazy Tabby Haikus

A lazy tabby
It has a furry black tail,
Always miaowing.

Lying on a bed
Snoring like a fuzzy bear,
What a lazy cat!

Charlotte Lawley (11)
Rough Hay Primary School

Pandas Haikus

A lazy panda
With black and white stripy stripes
Eating sweet bamboo.

Climbing up the tree,
Digging nails into the bark,
Now he can't get down!

Jack Watts (11)
Rough Hay Primary School

Pandas Haikus

Black and white pandas
Eating sweet bamboo all day,
Caring for their cubs.

Climbing up tall trees,
Drinking water from their leaves,
Big or small they're cute.

Jade Perry (10)
Rough Hay Primary School

Snow

Snow is like crystals which shimmer in the night-time cold.
Snow covers the world.
Summer life is about to die.
Winter life comes alive.
Children touch the snow mounds,
Making snowballs to throw at each other.
Snow is about having fun.
We all hope it lasts.

Alannah Cossey (8)
Woodlands Primary School

Teacher, Teacher

Teacher, Teacher, can I go to the toilet?
No you can't.
Teacher, Teacher, that boy is bothering me.
Go and work somewhere else then.
Teacher, Teacher, he is pulling faces at me.
Turn round then.
Teacher, Teacher, they are all talking.
Go and work in the hall, or the Head's office,
Just don't bother me!

Bobby Carver (10)
Woodlands Primary School

Sisters

Being one of four sisters,
You'll understand our house is never still,
Fighting for the TV remote,
Who's watching Corrie or The Bill!
We argue over toys,
Books and make-up too,
When Mum asks, 'Who's that shouting?'
We hush up and don't say boo.
Hard work we are sometimes,
That's what my mum thinks,
But us sisters love each other
And wouldn't change a thing.

Courtney Guy (9)
Woodlands Primary School

Animals

A is for antelope, whose spirits are free,
N is for newt, who is very wee,
I is for iguana, whose colours may vary,
M is for monkey, who is very hairy,
A is for ant who likes to crawl,
L is for leopard who is having a brawl,
S is for snake who slithers along,
   and opens its mouth and hisses its tongue.

Joseph Davies (10)
Woodlands Primary School

The Monster In The Loo

The monster in the loo is always there,
You can't help but stop and stare.
So you try to flush him down the loo,
But the monster already knew,
So he jumps out and gobbles you!

James Moore (9)
Woodlands Primary School

Mr Snow

Mr Snow brings the snow, you know,
And drops a cold, white blanket on the world.
It reminds me of a cake.
He sprinkles sugar on the cake and puts it in to bake.
Once the cake is ready, he makes a statue and puts it on the top,
He then adds some houses and lots and lots of hills.
Mr Snow puts adults and animals too.
He specially includes children to make them say *boo!*

Natalie Carless (9)
Woodlands Primary School

Food Poem

S tringy
P asta
A nd
G iant
H andfuls
E verywhere
T asting
T errific
I rresistible.

Lee Tranter (9)
Woodlands Primary School

Hide-And-Seek

I will hide,
You can seek,
Count to ten,
Please don't peek.
Behind a door,
Under a tree,
I can hide,
Can you see me?

Kimberley Smith (8)
Woodlands Primary School

Summer Season

Summer is the greatest season,
And dogs backs have fleas on.
Summer days are so great,
I can play out with my mate.

Summer means tennis is in,
I relish football's sin.
I love playing in the heat,
Joint with sweaty feet.

Summer's night breeze is cool,
When I'm up, I've got no school.
Summer is oh so fun,
I dread when it's done.

Summer comes again next year,
I bet there'll be a use of beer.
There's an end to every time,
Just like every rhyme.

Ryan O'Brien (11)
Woodlands Primary School

At The Pet Shop

There were fourteen dogs in the pet shop,
There were twenty bunnies going hop, hop, hop,
There were twenty-six blackbirds singing sweetly,
There were eleven lions roaring fiercely,
There were eighteen cats looking at the dogs,
There were seventeen, slimy, green frogs,
There were sixteen hyenas laughing loudly,
There were forty giraffes looking proudly,
There were twelve tigers licking their paws,
There were thirteen cheetahs sharpening their claws,
There were fifteen monkeys not making a peep,
There were all the animals fast asleep.

Jodie Aris (11)
Woodlands Primary School

My Family And Pet

Muscat is big and brown,
When he's sick it makes me frown.
He jumps up at me and I laugh out loud,
When he's better it makes me proud.
My great nan is the oldest,
At the age of 79.
When I stay at her house,
We have a marvelous time.
Next is grandad at 59,
A sensitive fellow, loving and fine.
He makes me laugh, always having fun,
Especially when surfing or lying in the sun.
Daddy, he is strong and bold,
He keeps us warm when we're very cold.
He looks after me very well,
How much I love him I'll never tell.
Mummy, she's always there for me,
When I'm feeling down,
But somehow, I don't know how,
She never makes me frown.
Dad's girlfriend, Vickie, looks after me,
We have such a laugh now she's learning to ski.
Brothers and sisters, I have quite a few,
Liam, Nathan, Abi and Amber too.
Liam is eight, he annoys me sometimes,
Nathan is three, we sing silly rhymes.
In America, there's Amber and little Abi,
I wonder if they all miss me?
Last of all, let's not forget me,
I'm hungry now, it's time for tea!

Kayleigh Hill (8)
Woodlands Primary School